CONTENTS

Be a Successful Writer

Acknowledgements

We acknowledge with grateful thanks the friendship, generous support and part-sponsorship of this anthology by

Antony Rowe Ltd

We are also indebted to the contribution of the following generous sponsors of the competitions who encourage creativity and writing excellence with all of its benefits well into the future:

Penguin UK
Piatkus Books
RPM Print and Design
Little Tiger Press-Magi
Writers'News-Writing
The Southern Daily Echo
Age Concern Hampshire
Little, Brown & Co. (UK)
Orion Publishing Group
Writers International Ltd
Queen's English Society
The Literacy Foundation
The British Haiku Society
Hampshire County Council
Hodder & Stoughton Publishers
Hampshire & Isle of Wight Youth Options

WELCOME

BARBARA LARGE MBE FRSA

Dame Beryl Bainbridge, Honorary Patron

Welcome to the pages of this 24th anniversary volume. This unique anthology presents the Plenary Address, *Laying Yourself on the Line*, given by Kevin Crossley-Holland, which set the theme for the 24th Annual Writers' Conference and Bookfair on the weekend of 26-28 June, 2004 at University College Winchester. This edition also presents the first place winning entries of the fifteen writing competitions. The adjudication of the winning entries and the presentation of the prizes were given at the Writers' Awards Reception on Saturday evening, 25 June, followed by the Writers' Awards Dinner.

The standard of entries was very high: competition was very keen. The judges found it very difficult to choose the winning entries as they read through almost three thousand manuscripts sent from every part of the globe. They praised the ingenuity, technical skills, well developed narratives, vivid dialogue, dazzling imagery, clever plots and the professional presentation of the manuscripts.

The air was electric as entrants scanned the short lists, posted at 1300 on Saturday. Pseudonyms as creative as Bombazine Custard, Shenanighans and Hilda Gruntfuttock had tantalized the judges.

These excellent results have been triggered by themes set by our sponsors who challenge writers to fashion their eclectic ideas into prize winning entries. To have work recognized as excellent by professional authors, commissioning editors and literary agents not only provides encouragement to striving authors but also to have work published in this anthology offers a much needed stepping-stone toward mainstream publication. Congratulatory certificates have been sent to all of the authors named in this anthology and each entrant has received a critique.

Not all entrants can be winners but each entrant has benefited from the discipline of entering the competitions and the adjudications provided by the judges.

Readers of this book will benefit from the adjudicators' comments as benchmarks for their own writing in a variety of fiction and non-fiction genres.

On the following pages, you will be greatly influenced as you read Kevin Crossley-Holland's Plenary Address, spoken so eloquently and with such conviction, humour and passion. His practical advice, wit and commitment mark him as distinguished international literary figure. One listener liken his talk to the richest and most succulent fruit cake that she had ever eaten.

Those who attended the conference benefited from the experience of 62 leading authors, poets, playwrights, publishers, literary agents, book production specialists and commissioning editors who gathered to share their skills, knowledge and enthusiasm for writing toward the goal of excellence during informal talks, seminars, mini courses, workshops and one to one appointments.

They also found that it was enjoyable to be with like-minded people and to learn more about the craft of writing together in this friendly professional environment.

Perhaps you will enter the competitions and join us for this magnificent festival of writing when we meet again 24-26 June, 2005 to celebrate our 25th anniversary!

In the meantime, happy reading and continued success with your writing.

Barbara Large

Barbara Large MBE FRSA FUCW
Conference Director

Laying Yourself on the Line

Kevin Crossley-Holland
Internationally acclaimed poet and Prize winning author for children

Be a Successful Writer

ViewPoint

Keynotes of Kevin Crossley-Holland's Plenary Address

The act of writing is a skill, a craft, a discipline. It can be taught and learned, I write without music which interrupts the rhythms I hear in my head. I write longhand. And I use a fountain pen.

Part of the art of writing skilfully is to conceal the sweat that goes into it.

May I make a plea for you to use language that is tough, quick, clean, keen? Why use a long word when the right short one will do?

To be serious writers, we must be disciplined; we must make sacrifices in order to be able to write.

LAYING YOURSELF ON THE LINE

KEVIN CROSSLEY-HOLLAND

Ladies and Gentlemen! Dear Creatures! Good morning to you all.

When Barbara Large invited me to be your Plenary Speaker, I immediately thought of the Visitors' Book that I bought when I was appointed as a young editor, green and enthusiastic, at the publishing house of Macmillan.

The first writer to inscribe his name was the poet and critic Philip Hobsbaum. 'Philip Hobsbaum', he wrote, and then he added, 'How difficult to begin!' The second visitor to my office was the poet and art critic, Edward Lucie-Smith. 'Edward Lucie-Smith' he wrote, and then he paused and added, 'How difficult to follow!' Words that since then have sounded sometimes humble, sometimes arrogant, but anyhow witty!

Well! What I know is that it is difficult to follow not one but a brace of Dames! Dame Phyllis and Dame Beryl. I will do my best!

In the Dark

Several early Celtic sources describe the way in which oral storytellers composed their poems and tales. They lay in the dark with a large stone on their stomachs. They composed, literally, in the dark.

Henry James wrote: 'We work in the dark.'

And the recent Newbery Medal winner Linda Sue Park says, 'I don't write what I know; I write what I want to know.'

This is my first, simple point. Whether you are poets, novelists, short story writers, biographers, you simply cannot begin to know exactly what you're going to write before you write it. Your work is the product of an individual mind and heart and nervous system. It's an act of discovery. In my lucky novel *The Seeing Stone,* young Arthur de Caldicot says, 'I need to see what I write to know what I think.'

Your act of writing involves risk-taking. It implies going wrong as well as going right. That's why I've called this talk *Laying Yourself on the Line*.

My Childhood

I'm scarcely the best model to stand here in front of you. As a boy, I had little appetite for reading. In fact, I only remember reading one book with pleasure – but I read it one hundred times! *Our Island Story.* The stories of Boudicca and Alfred and the like... I did once borrow a book from the library, but you know what happens if you keep it for more than three weeks. I hid it from my guilty self. I found it again. A year later! Rapidly, I hid it again. I found it for a second time. Forty years later! What will they do with me, I wondered. Put me in prison? I took the book back to the little library in the Chiltern Hills from which I'd borrowed it, with a copy of each of my own books, by way of payment. And you know what? The library wasn't there. It had burned down.

'What's that to you?' an old man in the village asked me. 'They was only books.'

To me? A hole in the heart.

From my father, my sister and I, lying in our bunk beds, we heard folk tales. He used to sing-and-say them, accompanying himself on the Welsh harp. It was he who told me first that King Arthur lay asleep inside a hill, awaiting the day when he and his warriors would wake, and drive all those nasty Anglo-Saxons back into the cold North Sea. And I had not the slightest doubt that the hill in question was Whiteleaf Cross, rising up behind our little cottage.

At the bottom of the garden, beyond the gooseberry bushes, there was a shed, full of rusty bikes and flowerpots and half-empty paint pots and all the usual things you find in sheds. I coveted that place. And with my father, I built shelving in it, and converted it into what I grandly called my museum. I put into it potsherds, fossils, the odd coin or two – that sort of thing.

Like most kids, I was always strapped for cash. Then I hit on a plan. I advertised the museum on a large blackboard, up on the main road. MUSEUM, it read. ENTRANCE FREE. But there was another sign on the cottage gate, in a small and duplicitous hand. MUSEUM. ENTRANCE ONE PENNY. Visitors came. The first was the novelist Rumer Godden, and she put into my lead till thirty pence – for which reason I've always considered her one of the finest novelists in the English language! The second visitor was an old family friend, Jacob Bronowski, and he was not going to be outdone by Rumer.

One day, my grandfather bought a rusty old shield in a local junk shop and gave it to me for my museum . 'Why not polish it up?' he said. 'You never know'.

I polished the rim. Stars. Scimitars. I polished the centre: a scowling face. My father and I took it to the Armoury at the Tower of London. They declared it to be a Saracen shield – a 12th century shield that must have been brought home by a crusader. Who and where and why and how and when? My shield and my museum, they were my point of ignition.

The Point of Ignition

This point of ignition is what each of us has to find for herself, himself. It's a matter of tuning in to oneself. Leslie Stephen wrote, very truly I think, that 'Originality does not consist in saying what no-one has ever said before, but in saying exactly what you think yourself.'

Some of you, of course, do already know exactly where you're heading, and many of you will have a sense of the shape of things, but some of you – especially the poets, maybe – have to wait patiently, knowing you're capable of writing something electric if only, if only, you knew precisely what you should be writing about.

Am I teaching you to suck eggs if I simply describe several simple ways I use to reach the point of ignition?

Here's one. Once, visiting a school, I nicked an apple from the head teacher's office. I put it on a table in a classroom. 'I can see it's round and green and so on,' I said to a class of ten-year-old children.

'Tell me something else about this apple. Surprise me! ('Étonne-moi!' as Diaghilev said to Jean Cocteau). One girl put up her hand. 'It'll weep if you bite it,' she said. This apple! It'll weep if you bite it. 'It's speckled,' said another. 'And freckled,' added a third, 'and like a sphere.' A fourth girl said, 'Well, it's got these pips inside it, dark pips.' 'What are they like, these pips?' I asked her. 'Well - they're hidden, like secrets.'

So there we had it – an apple on the table, that weeps if you bite it, and is speckled and freckled, and like a sphere, and contains dark secrets.

That's one way I use. Making associations. Making connections. Metaphors.

Another way is to reach back into the precious quarry – and each of us has it – the quarry of our childhood. Have you ever sat down and in three minutes, four minutes drawn a map of a childhood place: your house, your own room, the roads and lanes and houses of your friends, the places where you met? Draw it, quickly. Now latch on to something there that really matters to you. Now write about it. I dare you! You are the story. Yes, you are the story.

Or again, consider this. We're in Winchester, so rich in England's story. But the whole of England is rich in associations, rich in layers of language and story and coinage and laws, rich in the truths of the lie the land! True, Alan Brownjohn amusingly wrote, 'I have made England almost unusable with associations,' but how about turning things the other way round? What can you excavate from the layers of England? From being here, in this ancient and modern place? Then and now: the continuous interaction.

Or how about simply reading the work of another author? This too, is a proper, fruitful, even crucial way to bring yourself to a point of ignition. So that you can scarcely bear to go on reading and need to take over yourself. Remember, anyhow, what Dr Johnson said: 'I never desire to converse with a man who has written more than he has read.'

Process

The artist John Constable once described his process as 'legitimate, scientific, and mechanical.' I like that very much indeed. The act of writing is a skill, a craft, a discipline. It can be taught and learned, and I suppose we all share that view to some extent, otherwise we would not be here.

What was it Horace said? Festina Lente! Hurry slowly. Learn to unhurry. How right he was. I've always liked quick results but, as a writer, there is *no such thing*. In a sense, you have to proceed by indirection. This is how Michael Ondaatje (author of *The English Patient*) puts it: 'The first sentence of every novel should be, Trust me, this will take time, but there *is* order here, very faint, very human. Meander if you want to get to town.'

You could say that, in their own ways, storytelling and writing poetry are acts of complication. Novels address but do not answer issues: they complicate them. Poems offer insights by telling it slant, by what they say and what they do *not* say.

Apparent Simplicity

The last thing we want is for our prose or verse to appear to be heavily worked, the product of little more than method and worthy diligence. Part of the art of writing skilfully is to conceal the sweat that goes into it. This is what W. B. Yeats meant when we wrote, 'All this stitching and unstitching is worth naught unless it seem but a moment's thought.'

Lightness of touch almost invariably delights a reader. Because she/he is not being told what to think or feel and is free to imagine and empathise. Free to meet the writer halfway. We have to write with sufficient confidence and skill to allow our readers to do this.

I'm under no illusions about how difficult this is. When I write, I giddy round and round in circles like a dog – an old dog! – before it decides how to lie down.

A very quick word about my own writing practise: I begin early in the morning, working on the principle that the day deteriorates. I write when I can in my own little North Norfolk study. I write without music

which interrupts the rhythms I hear in my head. I write longhand. And I use a fountain pen.
For me, a first draft is exactly that. I revise and revise. Much as I admire the poetry of R.S. Thomas, I cannot relate to the way in which he elected not to revise because he could never return to the state of 'heightened consciousness' in which he was writing. I am of the school and persuasion of Robert Graves, who reworked his poems over and again. Of my father, I wrote:

> You thinned my words like seedlings. *And avoid*
> *long words where short suffice*. (Work; will do)
> For vogue and buzz and all-too-commonplace
> you wrote in almost timeless substitutes
> (ex-Yeats, ex-Graves). *Revise and then revise.*
> *Our second thoughts strike deeper than the first.*
>
> Sometimes you mused aloud, or asked me how
> my craft related to the science of sound -
> abstract in this, its power akin to music.
> *And sound*, you told me then, *includes silence.*
> One part of the performance, integral...
> I hear myself. Hear all that's left unsaid.

'To write simply', said Somerset Maughan, 'is as difficult as to be good.' Just so!

Language

This brings me to the matter of language.

We humans use language each day, all day. It is part of what distinguishes us from the croaking, neighing, braying, barking animal world. But as you know, use implies abuse. All around us, we hear and see language abused. Language is a beauty and a beast. You are its custodians.

The English language is by far the most flexible of world languages.

It has over well 60,000 words, more than double that of any other language, because it derives from both Anglo-Saxon and Latin (via Norman French). It's Anglo-Saxon that gives us the words to do with the stuff of life – womb, woman, man, heart, earth, sky, sea, ship, plough, etc. May I make a plea for you to use language that is tough, quick, clean, keen? Why use a long word when the right short one will do?

Collegiate

Many years ago, I asked the poet Peter Porter to sign one of his books for me.

'From Peter Porter,' he wrote, 'with collegiate greetings.' At the time, I thought the choice of adjective strange; now I find it utterly appropriate.

In my experience, the literary world *is* collegiate, that is to say mutually supportive, to a degree the musical and fine arts worlds are not! Of course, there's some back-biting and jealousy, but when you really need advice, support, you're likely to find people willing to give generously of their time and experience.

And of course, this readiness to share is the very lifeblood of this tremendous conference.

Story and Poems as Revelation

Au fond, stories and poems show us what it is like to be a human being. They give us back ourselves. 'The only end of writing,' Dr Johnson said, 'is to enable the reader better to enjoy life or better to endure it.' This pronouncement was echoed by Lord Reith when he articulated the principles of the BBC as being to educate and to entertain.

This idea of story and poem leading to self-discovery is what I was after in my *Arthur* trilogy. A boy called Arthur de Caldicot, growing up at the beginning of the 13th century, looks into a hunk of obsidian and begins to see in it the story of his namesake, Arthur the king. And this story of the boy king seems somehow to anticipate and reflect his own hopes, longings, frustrations, anxieties.

With self-understanding comes *empowerment*. We recognise we live in a world ennobled by human dream and ideal, fatally flawed by human weakness. Like Camelot, in fact. Empowered we remain ready to question, and recognise the crucial importance of questioning if we are not only to look but to see, not only to listen but to hear. And with empowerment, we believe each one of us can and must make a difference:

Sister Cika told me Saracens and Jews believe a person who saves the life of another saves the whole world. I believe that too. I believe each of us can make a difference.

It's people like Wido and Godard and Giff, following each other like cattle, never questioning, never thinking for themselves, becoming numb to bloodshed and other people's pain, who turn our world into a wasteland.

Sir John's right. Each person does have his own position, her own duties – in a family, a manor, a kingdom. But what I want at Catmole is one fellowship. One ring of trust. I want everyone in the manor to know we all need each other and each one of us makes a difference.

Privilege and Discipline

W. B. Yeats, the poet I loved above all others throughout my twenties, wrote 'All things can tempt me from this craft of verse.' How true! We all know it to be true. To be serious writers, we must be disciplined; we must make sacrifices in order to be able to write.

I don't underestimate how terribly difficult it can be for people to square a longing to write with their other responsibilities – to children, to elderly parents, to people who need looking after, to their day-jobs. But try to treat writing as some people treat prayer and as all of us treat eating, part of a daily process.

In the end, it's rather a privilege to be a writer, isn't it? You're involved in a solitary act with social implications. An act that for all its frustrations can be deeply rewarding. There can be very great pleasure, in sharing, and in recognition; but for me, it's the *process* itself – planning, drafting, revising – that is truly fulfilling.

Have you read that wonderful anatomy of a Suffolk village, *Akenfield,* in which Ronald Blythe talks to villagers about their lives and jobs. 'What was the song, Davie?' he asks one old man who used to take part in village sing-songs. 'Never mind the song,' Davie replies. 'It was the singing that counted.'

Envoi

A couple of nights ago my wife and I went to the Aldeburgh Festival – a concert at Snape. It was a rough-gruff night, a wild night. The old Maltings creaked and groaned a little.

In their bright pool of light, the trio were so busy – and yet so still. So attentive, that is. So focused, in their own storm of variations, arguments, conflicts, resolutions.

I thought about giving this talk and saw these three musicians as a kind of conceit, a model for any maker or remaker, anywhere. In this world and out of it, recreating it.

With music, then, and with images, and for each of us here with words: lay yourself on the line! Let there be light!

Be a Successful Writer

ViewPoint

The Plenary Address given by Kevin Crossley-Holland was a total delight, with personal touches that were charming glimpses of a man who is a genuine master of his craft.

I was on the same wave length as Kevin Crossley-Holland: the inspirational way he looks at objects and draws maps to support his writing.

I felt like a child in an ice cream shop: so spoilt for choice as to which courses to choose at the conference.

Inspiration is an important component of the creative process but I have learned so much more during this exciting and informative weekend.

It is a joy to see so many people getting so much creative stimulation out of one weekend! An encouraging atmosphere abuzz with writers.

Short Story Competition

Sponsors:

World Wide Writers

A Showcase for The Best Short Fiction

Adjudicator: John Jenkins

WINNERS & HIGHLY COMMENDED

Competitors were invited to submit quality short stories on any subject, theme or period. Length 1500-3000 words. Entries were judged on their originality, entertainment value and excellent storytelling qualities.

Winners

	Prize	Title	Author / *Pseudonym*
1st	**£200**	**The Seagull**	**Pam Baddeley** *Dark Willow*
2nd	**£75**	**The Bridge**	**Alison Marlow** *Muzzy*
3rd	**£50**	**Wrong Number**	**Cynthia Chapman** *Bluey*

Highly Commended

Title	Author	Pseudonym
Mrs Astaire	**Elaine McCulloch**	*M. Keir*
The Night of the Fish	**Pat Wells**	*Tapper*
One Brown, One Blue	**Sarah Cuthbertson**	*Freya Cooper*
A Sign of Old Age	**Sylvia Mitchell**	*Early Bird*
A Room With a View	**Alison Theaker**	*Alison Appleby*
Love Plus	**Anne Brooke**	*Dreamer*
Just Deserts	**Pat Wells**	*Tapper*
Sins of Omission	**Tamsin Reeves**	*Judy Green*
The Purdey	**Karen Meredith**	*Honey Potts*
Maisie and Her Jumper	**Jennifer Margrave**	*M O'Shennighans*

[Editor's note: The Seagull was published in the Writers' Forum magazine, August 2004 edition

THE SEAGULL

PAM BADDELEY

It was a golden summer that year, just me and the Seagull and the clear blue waters of Coniston. The last summer, before war swept away innocence and solitude and the joy of running before the wind, my hand on the tiller, Seagull's sails ballooning as she carried me onward. Days of safety and of parents who loved you and loved each other. Days lost forever. And all due to my own stupidity.

Funny. They're right when they say childhood is always clearest to the old. When I look back across sixty-five years to those last weeks before the war, it seems a bright place surrounded by darkness. Was the sky always so blue, the waters a gentle swell before a wind that was always dependable, the surrounding hills a glowing green? If there were clouds, they were there only to paint shadows on those hills, to play with colour and light as if the uplands lay under the hand of a skilled artist.

I was always out on the lake. I'd rush out after breakfast with a packed lunch my mother made, and would stay out till tea. So many things were different then. They'd never let a twelve year old boy go out in a boat on his own now, would they? Was it normal then? It was to me. After all, the Swallows and Amazons spent all their time boating with no grown-ups to spoil the fun. Sometimes I liked to pretend I was one of them, Seagull another boat in their flotilla. Or maybe we'd hold a race, the Walkers just alongside me in the Swallow, Nancy and Peggy a neck behind, straining with all their skill to overtake. But I'd nudge ahead, reach the imaginary finishing line a prow ahead of everyone else. We'd shake hands afterwards of course, congratulate each other on a good race fairly fought. But usually it was just me and Seagull, navigating the familiar bays, crossing the lake like Magellan, or drifting in the sun while I ate my sandwiches and drank from my flask of tea.

I say we were alone, just Seagull and me, but of course there were other people on the lake. A few were in boats and we'd exchange a wave or a shout of "Hello" but others could be seen as distant figures onshore. I would watch them, wondering what they were doing or thinking. If only I hadn't wanted to know. If I hadn't, that brilliant summer wouldn't have been lost in darkness.

It started when I first saw the boat. It was moored by one of the islands in the lake. I'd scrambled ashore there myself once, after making Seagull safe to one of the branches that dipped low over the water. I'd squeezed through bushes and stubby trees, imagining myself as Livingstone, advancing through the African jungle. The secret heart of the island opened before me, a small grove of scanty grass. I suppose it was large enough for three people to sit around a picnic, if they were close friends. It was hemmed in and overhung by branches, not an inviting place, so I'd left disappointed. What could someone be doing there? That first time, I only noted it as I sailed past, the way I noted everything on my lake.

But it was there again, two days later, and then the day after that, always in the early afternoon, as I knew by the sun's height. And when I sailed past on my way home for tea each day, it was gone. Slowly, the urge to discover just what was so interesting about the island began to consume me. Rumours had penetrated even my tranquil surroundings, got through even my general indifference to the complicated and baffling world of grown-ups. People said there could be war. So the answer to the mystery seemed obvious: spies. Germans, or people working for them. The idea grew, and as I drifted off to sleep one night, I decided I had to find out. I don't know what I thought spies could be doing in a sleepy place like Lake Coniston but to my young mind, it was the only explanation that made sense.

So that's why I headed straight for the island the next morning, to find what the spies had hidden at its heart. It had to be a radio.

But when I landed I found only flattened grass. Baffled, I looked around then my heart jumped as I spotted something thrust into a crook of one of the low trees. I reached up and grabbed it, my hands encountering wool. A rolled up blanket. The radio! But it was too light, and when I unrolled it on the ground there was nothing inside. I crouched over it, disbelieving. What could someone be doing here with this? The place was too cut off from the sky for sunbathing. Feeling cheated, I rolled up the blanket and replaced it.

I looked around again at the patch of grass, anxious to spot a clue. Then I saw a small white object. I picked it up. A cigarette end. And another. The second one had a smudge of pink, and I realised it must be lipstick.

My spirits rose. Now I was Sherlock Holmes. There must be two people, a man and a woman. A vague sensation that I had stumbled upon some adult mystery troubled my mind. Of course, how could any modern child fail to realise what had been happening in this isolated spot? But you must realise that, in those days, we were children for a lot longer. So I dropped the cigarette ends and pushed my way back to the water's edge, clambered into Seagull and shoved off with an oar, raising the sail again when I got clear of the outreaching branches.

I didn't come back that day. But the next afternoon, the mystery boat was in its usual place. I had to know. I lowered Seagull's sail and used the oars to glide in, till I could reach the same overhanging bough where the other boat was moored. I tied Seagull's painter, then stepped into the other boat. As I grasped a higher branch and was about to lift my foot, I glanced down. Draped across the seat was a silk scarf.

I froze. The pattern of pink carnations against pale green was familiar. My mother had a scarf like this. But it couldn't be hers. She couldn't handle a boat for one thing. And she was at home, busy doing something: getting tea, making preparations for dinner when my father got home, doing whatever mothers did when they were alone. I shrugged off the odd feeling the scarf had given me and stepped ashore.

Now I moved with exaggerated care, sure that a twig would snap under my foot as I crept nearer to the spies' hide-out. I listened hard, sure they must be reporting to HQ on their radio, but all I could hear was the gentle lap of water behind me against the edge of the island and the hulls of the two boats.

The tiny glade was before me and now I could peer between the leaves. At first, my eyes were still adjusting to the gloom. But I could hear something: odd sounds like someone trying to regain their breath. A sigh. Moans.

And then I could see a man's back. A hand clasped it, a stray speck of light glinting from a band around one finger. A ring. The back and the hand were moving.

I leaned forward, trying to see more, suddenly aware I was witness to a forbidden adult secret I'd sniggered and wondered about with other boys at school. Here were people 'doing it'.

A twig snapped. They heard me, because the woman gave a startled cry.

I don't remember a lot after that. Only the look of horror on my mother's face. I can't recall his face at all, still don't know if I even saw it. All I remember is blundering back to Seagull and somehow getting her untied. The next thing I recall is being halfway across the lake, frantically rowing as if the hounds of hell were behind me.

The next few days are a blur. She didn't have to tell my father. She must have realised I wouldn't. Couldn't. But I think she told him that night. All I know is, she was red-eyed next morning when she told me I had to go away for a while, to stay with my aunt and uncle in Chester. I knew it was my fault, felt with a child's instinct that something dark and terrible had happened. I know now that my parents' marriage was over.

The announcement about the war soon afterwards seemed part of the general catastrophe that swept me away to Chester. Then Father joined the army and was killed at Dunkirk. Just after that, my aunt got a letter: Mother had gone back to her parents in London and the house had taken a direct hit.

If my thoughtless curiosity had not drawn me to the island, would Father have joined up so soon, might he have missed Dunkirk, survived? I knew it was all my fault. A golden world, snatched away.

Everything gone: Mother, Father, Coniston and Seagull. When I made my way back after the war, all I found was the rotting remains of the little jetty where I used to keep her tied up, a frayed rope all that was left of her. Now she sails only in my memories and dreams. Seagull, child of a golden summer.

Adjudication

Let me say at once that the good were very good, most were good and a few were awful. It still surprises me to discover that writers who expect to get a story published and who are meticulous in their day-to-day lives can present careless work. The authors of the stories who placed first, second and third, can feel justly proud while the remainder who achieved highly commended should consider submitting their work for publication. They were that good!

The Seagull *was nostalgic, atmospheric, beautifully paced and crafted.*

The Bridge *was emotional, thought-provoking, well written and well worth publishing.*

Wrong Number *was a story for today, well paced, suitable for any number of magazines.*

There was hardly a sliver of difference between the Highly Commended and the second and third choices.

John Jenkins

A Few Tips on Editing

The best writers rewrite. They do not expect to get it right the first time. Many beginning writers do no more than get a good idea, make a few notes and then write it. Whether you are writing for a publisher or a competition you must be your own exacting editor. You must methodically check every word. Do you go through the story line by line or do you just run it through the spell checker?
Has the author achieved what he set out to do? Has he entertained the reader? Has he made the reader think? Has he informed the reader? Or has he written a dressed -up anecdote or some episodic adventure?

Consider this checklist: writers who aspire to be successful should ask the following questions:

Opening: Is it dynamic? Does it set the scene? Does it grab the reader, demanding that he should read on? Three quarters of any editor's work concerns beginning and endings. Without a good opening, your story will sink into the reject pile.

Title: Original? Hackneyed? Provocative?

Characters: Stories must be character-driven. We are talking about homo fictus, not homo sapiens. Memorable characters must be larger than life. What about your subordinate characters? Somebody has to get the Oscar for best supporting actor. Too many beginners neglect the subsidiary characters in their stories.

Theme: Are you writing about something that really matters? This is as germane for a story in The Lady or The New Yorker as it is for competitions.

Entertainment: P D James once said that when she realized that she was in the entertainment business she began to succeed. You make a contract with the reader, your story is his time and money. Is he getting a good deal?

Dialogue: Is it obvious who is speaking if you remove all the he saids /she saids. It should be. If not, rewrite it. Record and listen to it.

Language: Writers are the guardians of the English language. If you break the rules, know why you are doing it. Poets know that they want the perfect word in the perfect place. It's no surprise that many good poets are good tellers of short stories.

The Ending: It should not fizzle out. It should not be an anticlimax. It should not be revealed as a dream. Have you answered the basic Kipling questions: who, what, where, why, when and how?
Have you utilized the senses; sight, smell, taste, hearing, touch and that crime fiction author's favourite, the sixth sense.

Elmore Leonard, one of America's finest crime writers suggests that aspiring authors should go easy on the adverbs, exclamation marks and especially the hooptedoodle.

In Steinbeck's Sweet Thursday, a character says 'Sometimes I want a book to break loose with a bunch of hooptedoodle – spin up some pretty words, maybe sing a little song with language but I don't want it to interfere with the story line'.

Elmore Leonard's most important rule is this: if it sounds like writing, rewrite it. We cannot allow what we learned in English language classes to disrupt the sound and rhythm of the narrative. It is the author's job to remain invisible, not to distract the reader with obvious writing.

Just remember; Go easy on the hooptedoodle: or as we would say, fine writing.

John Jenkins

Be a Successful Writer

ViewPoint

All of the writers deserve our thanks for being so willing to share their experience and knowledge with those of us who are still trying to get there . I very much hope that this will not be my last conference.

I was delighted to receive my manuscript and to read the response which was constructive and encouraging. It has given a focus to my editing and revising process which is very helpful and makes me very glad to be part of such a strong and supportive network. Thank you!

Jude Evans and her team at Little Tiger Press took the trouble to write an in-depth appraisal for each entrant in their competition, giving the strengths and weaknesses of the work. What tremendous commitment to us as fledgling writers.

Poetry Competition

Sponsor:

SOUTHERN
Daily Echo

Writing Excellence is Our Business

Adjudicator: Phil Carradice

WINNERS & HIGHLY COMMENDED

Competitors were invited to submit poems on any subject up to a maximum of 40 lines for each entry.

Winners

	PRIZE	TITLE	AUTHOR / *PSEUDONYM*
1st	**£150 & the Echo Trophy**	**The Black Morning**	**Lorna Howarth** *Rosie Hammond*
2nd	**£100**	**Of Hearts and Flowers**	**Judith Allnatt** *Sargasso*
3rd	**£75**	**Bookends**	**Mike Greenhough** *Barrington Thripp*

Highly Commended

TITLE	AUTHOR	PSEUDONYM
Redbridge	**Denis Pentlow**	*Micro*
Legend	**Anne Brooke**	*Dreamer*
Love Rat	**Lynda O'Neill**	*Marion*
End of Season	**Pam Nixon**	*Margaret Evelyn*
20-20 Vision	**Tony Corbin**	*Epouion*
Silence; Snow	**Jennifer Margrave**	*M O'Shennighans*

The winning poem was inspired by Mary Princes' own story when she was a slave in Bermuda in the early 19th century.

Editor's note:The winning poem will be printed in the Southern Daily Echo in January, 2005

THE BLACK MORNING

LORNA HOWARTH

The morning comes, too soon,
My mother shrouds us in our osnabergs
new for the vendue
carries her little chickens to the market place.

I hear her weeping as she lines us up
me the eldest first
our backs against the wall.
She motions us to fold our arms across our breasts.

White men handle and examine us
like butchers
pluck and pinch our flesh
curl back our lips and count our teeth.

Then the vendue master takes me by the hand
Leads me to the middle of the street
and I remember happy days
when Miss Betsey used to lead me by the hand
her little nigger.

Their circle closes and I am slowly turned
while eyes judge the shape and strength of my calves
the length and line of my naked back.

Their words and laughter fall like cayenne
on the fresh wounds of our hearts.

ADJUDICATION

This is an excellent free verse poem, tightly written with barely a word out of place and with imagery that catches perfectly the sense of time and place. It is tight writing at its very best. Above all, it is a good example of emotion driving a poem but emotion that is held in check by the choice of words and by the fact that so much is left to implication not drawn out or detailed for the reader. That would have been too much and the power of the emotion would have over-run into sentiment. As it is, the poet gets it just right; the balance between showing and telling. Prose writers could learn so much about that crucial technique simply by reading this poem. There are some wonderful images here: 'Their words and laughter fall like cayenne / on the fresh wounds of our hearts' Or again, 'White men handle and examine us / like butchers / pluck and pinch our flesh/curl back our lips and count our teeth.'

The power to shock is important in a poem like this. After all, that is what it is really all about. But the phrase used in the middle of the poem: 'her little nigger' comes like a sudden and unexpected punch in the belly. It is excellently done.

If I had one gripe, it would be the footnote that tells me that the poem is about Mary Prince, a slave in Bermuda in the 19th century. Carping I may be, but the poem does not need it. It is strong enough to stand on its own.

Phil Carradice

The First Three Pages of a Novel Competition

Sponsors:

PIATKUS

Piatkus Books – where every book is special

Adjudicators: Gillian Green & Emma Callagher

Sally Spedding, Julia Bryant, Mary Cross,

Angela Arney, Jeannie Johnson, Catherine Jones

WINNERS & HIGHLY COMMENDED

Competitors were invited to send the first three pages of a novel (maximum 5000 words) plus a two page synopsis of the novel. Any theme or period.

Winners

	PRIZE	TITLE	AUTHOR / *PSEUDONYM*
1st	**£75 book prize and the Nancy Smith Memorial Trophy**	**Mermaid**	**BronwenGriffiths** *Mary Baron*
2nd	**£50 book prize**	**Pasta Joke**	**Ghislaine Goff** *Lilac Pond*
3rd	**£25 book prize**	**An Uncertain Glory**	**Eve Phillips** *Viola*

Highly Commended

TITLE	AUTHOR	PSEUDONYM
A Squeal of Brakes	**Stuart Rickard**	*John Beaton*
Strangers and Pilgrims	**Sarah Austin**	*Whippet*
Karma	**Jennifer Marlow**	*M O'Shenanighans*
Undertow	**Alison Theaker**	*Alison Appleby*
Uncle Robert	**J D Mackereth**	*Bob Atkinson*
Searching for Athena	**Ghislaine Goff**	*Lilac Pond*
The West in Her Eyes	**Jay Ellis**	*Janet Hancock*
A Heart Alone	**Heather Moorland**	*Hazel Martell*
Rough	**E M Jolly**	*Mark Antony*
Stalker	**Evelyn Harris**	*Chris Lewis*
Something Beginning with B	**E Robertson**	*Vanessa Downs*
Flesh	**Alex Swinburn**	*AlexRomanovsky*
It Was a May Day	**Sheila Black**	*Fatso Inkwell*

[Editor's note: The beautifully hand-crafted Nancy Smith Memorial Trophy is presented annually in loving memory of their mother by The Smith Family.]

MERMAID

Bronwen Griffiths

'He was just bigger than a blenny.' Nana said.

'What's a blenny?'

'A small fish'.

His Nana would know that, coming, not from the sprawling industrial town with its belching steelworks but from some gentler place.

A sparkly place; all blue, like a marble.

'Tell me, Nana.' Twice a year she'd visit. Every time he'd plead; almost go hoarse with it.

'We've mermaids with cruel hearts, fishermen with grey beards long as rope, more pebbles than the whole world, the sea deeper than heaven itself.'

'Have you seen a mermaid, Nanna?'

'Of course.'

Stop filling him full of tales,' his mother would say, bringing in the washing, complaining about the smuts on the sheets.

'They're not tales,' Nana would snort. She'd drop her voice; whisper the story about the fisherman who caught a fish the size of a whale, the mermaid who wept so much when she broke her mirror that the sea rose and drowned several islands. Once, when his mother went to the corner shop for a packet of Woodbines, she put her hand in that large battered bag she always carried and fished something out.

'See, Nelson.' She sounded triumphant, as though she'd won on the bingo. She'd always called him Nelson, even though it was only a middle name. 'A witch's stone.'

He held out his hand. The stone smelled of the peppermints and throat lozenges. It wasn't much different from the pebbles in the garden, just grey and brown, but for one thing, a perfect hole. He poked his finger through it, wore it like a heavy ring.

'Put you eye to the hole. You'll see into the future.'

Nelson weighed the stone in his right hand, then the left. It turned steadily warmer. He closed one eye, stared through the hole. The room receded. He thought he saw his mother return, yet she seemed shrunken, like a toy. Her hair was a white as snow.

Later he tried it out in the garden. Everything looked faraway and shimmering, as though he was underwater, like in a bath.

'Take me to see the mermaids.'

It was his mother who always said no.

That July he came up to six. He doesn't remember the day, the cake, and the presents. His father gave him a fort he'd built out of plywood. 'With a dozen red soldiers,' his mother reminds him years afterwards. The memory is gone, eclipsed by what came later.

'I'm taking you to the Point.' Nana says. He thinks of the place as sharp, like a needle.

Now he's travelling a thousand miles, it seems, of railway track. The train edges out of the city, passing the gas towers and the brewery, the chewing cows and the canal with its long red and black boats. It gathers up speed, they fly through towns and villages, squares of green. Nana produces a soggy sandwich and a cup of sweet but barely warm tea. He fidgets; Nana sleeps. Dribble forms at the corner of her mouth.

They arrive in another great city crowded with people and more cars than he'd ever seen. They board a red bus, another train. Slowly the landscape turns soft and quiet. A church spire intrudes into the sky like a giant's finger. He falls asleep and when he awakes, the rolling hills and valleys, like crinkles in a blanket, have been smoothed out. Outside, it's flat as a tabletop.

The fields are sliced through with ribbons of water and there are pools everywhere, like dozens of eyes. Ducks fly up, scared by the wheezing train. Seagulls bob up and down in the billowing smoke. A thousand sheep, like tiny white sweets, are scattered across the endless grass.

They alight at a small station. Everyone gets off, laughing, chattering. The women are wearing hats and summer dresses; they smell like his mother after her weekly bath.

'Not long now, Nana says. She's been saying the same for hours.

This train is small, as though it were made for him, with wooden benches and brass fittings. He presses his face against the window as the driver hoots the horn. The train moves off, chugging peacefully across the empty , flat land. Horses graze in the fields, there are wooden shacks, a huddle of caravans. The fields turn stony: they pass a row of bungalows.

Synopsis

The Point is scarcely more than a sea-bitten piece of shingle, surrounded by marshland and endless sky. It is here that Nelson lives, an odd- job man who paints mermaids in his spare time. Nelson shares an old fisherman's hut with his teenage nephew, Joe.

The novel starts at the beginning and the end: with Nelson's first visit to the Point, fifty years before, in the company of his beloved Nana and with Joe, who can't swim, wading onto a shingle bank and then into deep water.

When Nelson visited the Point as a child he saw a mermaid with mysterious green eyes sitting on the prow of a boat. On day, years later, when's he's married with two daughters, the mermaid slips back into his life in the guise of his future sister-in-law, Maisie.

Tragically, Joe's mother, the mermaid of Nelson's desire, was later killed in a house fire, together with her young daughter, Joe's sister. Joe's father vanished soon after the fire, leaving him in Nelson's care. Within weeks, they'd moved out of the city, down to the Point.

Seven years on, Nelson is growing old, while Joe is growing up; seeking to make sense of the past. He and Nelson still grieve for their lost family but neither talks about the loss, preferring to bury their true feelings.

One cold, grey day in late winter, a girl, Cassie, appears on the Point with their mother. They rent a wooden shack not far from the edge of the sea. It's not glamourous, as Cassie's mother puts it, but it's romantic.

ADJUDICATION

Our judges felt that this was a lovely, magical proposal with a great deal of charm and originality. Your writing is, perhaps, a little rough around the edges and would benefit from a closer eye but your 'voice' is very appealing. I would love to read more and would like to invite you to submit the first three chapters of your novel for our fiction department for further consideration..

Gillian Green & Emma Callagher

Nancy Smith – A Tribute:

Nancy Smith not only adjudicated this competition for many years but also she was an excellent speaker and keen supporter of this conference from its inception. Nancy was an author, published by Piatkus Books and a tutor who gave her time generously to help a generation of aspiring writers.

She is remembered with great affection and gratitude. Her memory will be kept alive by the annual presentation of the magnificent memorial trophy awarded by her family.

Writing Can Be Murder Competition

Sponsor:

OG

Orion Publishing Group

Adjudicator: Lesley Horton

WINNERS & HIGHLY COMMENDED

Competitors were invited to submit the first 500 words of a short story or novel with a murder thriller theme.

Winners

	PRIZE	TITLE	AUTHOR / *PSEUDONYM*
1st	**£100 book prize**	**The Chosen Ones**	**Linda Dunscombe** *Swann*
2nd	**£75 book prize**	**Dying To Tell**	**Giselle Finn** *Bag End*
3rd	**£50 book prize**	**The Long Game**	**Heather Mulkey** *Tindzaba*

Highly Commended

TITLE	AUTHOR	PSEUDONYM
A Traitor Among Us	**Lindsey Russell**	*Rufus*
Boys Will	**Alison Marlow**	*Muzzy*
Studying Form	**Evelyn Harris**	*Chris Lewis*
Circle Sisters	**Sarah Way**	*Ben Benson*
Not Always	**Pat Hillyer**	*Platypus*
Redemption	**Linda Dunscombe**	*Swann*

THE CHOSEN ONES

LINDA DUNSCOMBE

The lad shivered. His fingers trembled. He shoved them into the pockets of his hooded jacket and glanced nervously across at the man.

They paused at the roadside. He let himself look up. He had been warned to keep his head down, be invisible. Never let the enemy see your face.

But he wanted to look. He loved the noise and the chaos of the heavy traffic, the smell of diesel and decay. Not the decay of death and poverty but of age and history.

It wasn't what he'd expected. Some of it was true. There was greed and decadence and indifference. But there was also kindness and compassion, which had taken him by surprise. Scared him if he was honest.

He had to concentrate, to focus. He couldn't let his family down. His sisters were promised good husbands. His younger brother would get a proper education. His mother could hold her head high and boast about her son.

He was struggling for breath. His lungs squeezed by unseen hands.

He stopped. Run, the voice in his head shouted. Now. Disappear.

He looked up as the man gripped his shoulder.

'It's okay, Ali', the man said leaning down. 'You're afraid?'

He nodded.

'So am I.'

Ali stared up at him. The man didn't look afraid. In fact, he looked calm and confident with his smart haircut and expensive clothes.

'Up here,' the man said, touching his head, 'the fear comes from the brain. But you have courage, Ali, follow your heart.'

Ali closed his eyes and took a deep breath.

The man gave him an encouraging nudge. He ran forward and jumped onto the red double-decker bus. He climbed the stairs and sat down at the back.

It was a mistake.

He had been told to sit at the front. He needed a clear view. He went to stand. But the bus braked and he stumbled. A young woman reached out her hand, offering him help.

He brushed her away, embarrassed and angry. For a fleeting second their eyes met. She was pretty in a pink and pale way.

Ali slunk down into his seat. The trembling was back. Violent shaking. His forehead was running with sweat. The bus was slowing. He looked out of the window. This was the stop. This was his moment. His time...

He reached into his pocket. The strap was dangling, Waiting...

The girl stood up. She glanced his way and smiled.

He gripped the leather trigger. He could hear her heels as she ran down the stairs. He could wait a few seconds.

He thought of his sisters with their solemn eyes and sleek long hair. He glanced once more out of the window. The girl was clear. Safe. Walking away...

Ali's head tried to dominate his will. Tried to tell him to take his hand off the strap and run for sanctuary to the nearest police station.

But his heart prayed to Allah and with an explosive tug he did what he had been chosen to do.

Adjudication

The Chosen Ones: I put this in first place for a variety of reasons. The topic is up to date. There's much discussion as to whether crime novels should make a statement, whether writers should look at what is happening in the world and incorporate it into a crime novel. I think there is no reason not to do this and done well, it works. This is what The Chosen Ones did, but from a different perspective: from the perspective of a young lad chosen to be a suicide bomber.
The writing is excellent and confident. The pace is exactly right. The reader feels the fear in the boy as well as the inevitability of what he has to do. Although by this end, he has pulled the strap and detonated the bomb, the reader knows what that took. We understand his confusion, appreciate his desire to make his family proud of him, observe his terror at what he is about to do and believe in his compassion for the young girl whom he allowed to be safe after she helped him when he stumbled as the bus braked.
Tension is heightened in the reader who is with him all the way, willing him not to sacrifice his young life by detonating the bomb but at the same time understanding why he has to do it, yet thanking him for the girl's safety.
His character is clearly defined, as is that of the man urging him on. The deed has to be carried out, but not by him. The boy is expendable. The man with the smart haircut and expensive clothes is not.
An excellent opening and a well deserved winner.

Lesley Horton

Be a Successful Writer

ViewPoint

I was so thrilled to be awarded first prize in The First Three Pages of the Novel Competition, having slogged it out for years.I suppose that's how life goes.

Thank you for sending my adjudication from Piatkus Books. I enjoyed reading the judges' assessments. It's good to learn what you did right as well as what you did wrong!

By any measure, you must have regarded this conference as a resounding success. For my own part, I was thrilled to meet so many professional writers who were willing to give up their time to help others on their way to success.

The unpretentious attitude of all of the speakers who so selflessly gave of their time, knowledge, experience and themselves to help people like me to develop our craft and careers was memorable.

Reaching Out Competition

Sponsor:

Penguin UK

Publishing Excellence

www.penguin.com

Adjudicator: Pat King

WINNERS & HIGHLY COMMENDED

Especially and only for those writers who would have liked to attend the conference but were prevented by distance, age or disablement. Specification: Any theme, up to 5000 words. Entrants submitted up to five poems or five short stories.

Winners

	Prize	Title	Author / *Pseudonym*
1st	**£60 book prize**	**Letters to a Soldier**	**Joy Harwood** *J J Denny*
2nd	**£30 book prize**	**The Box**	**Stephen Cole** *Stephanie*
3rd	**£20 book prize**	**Cold Roses**	**D J Russell** *J D Woodfield*

Highly Commended

Title	Author	Pseudonym
The Riverman	**Dhirendra Pattnaik**	*Bluebird*
The Eclipse of the Sun	**Marta Nagy**	*Rosemary Gibson*
Night Garden	**Ruth Clough**	*Penelope*
Dignified Nudity	**June Ayling**	*Smiler*

Editor's Note: The winners of the Reaching Out Competition have overcome communication and physical disabilities, to compete in this competition.For some ,who have difficulties in speaking, this competition offers the opportunity to participate and to achieve results which contribute greatly to their self-esteem and to their desire to continue with their writing.

LETTERS TO A SOLDIER

Joy Harwood

A good day, Mail Day, usually a Thursday for some reason, though you couldn't rely on it. Sometimes it came a day early, mostly it was late, Friday, Saturday, even Sunday. Someone up the line hadn't the first idea how much it mattered when you got your mail. Like today, the men sprawled out on their beds, feet up, an illusion of leisure, each one intent upon the enjoyment of a moment's privacy, a transportation to the place he called home. Or love nest, or hell hole, depending.

Con studied the envelope for a moment, then carefully folded it away in the inside pocket of his jacket. He knew the sort of thing the letter would say and he was in no hurry to read it. Although the longer he put it off the more it would tease him, so perhaps it couldn't wait. Either way, did it really matter?

'No mail, Con?' The man in the next bed leaned across, sorry for the poor sod. 'You can read one of mine, if you like!' he joked, fanning out the half dozen envelopes scattered on the bed.

Con waved the offer to one side. 'I've got one, thanks,' he said. 'Making it last, you could say.' He got to his feet and made for the door. He would take a walk while it was still daylight, open the letter when he was on his own, when he could more readily decide what his reaction was going to be.

'Dear Boy.' That's what she'd always called him, reducing him, making him feel small, less, somehow unimportant. At first it had been a joke between them.

'I'm nobody's boy!' he told her. 'Just you wait, young woman, till you see me in action!' and seeing her purse her lips, he winked to soften the crudity of the remark. But she still called him Boy.

Dear Boy,

Five weeks? It feels more like five months since you were here and the boys calling in of an evening, having a beer and a take-away round the TV. They still look in sometimes, one or two of them, Griff and Dave and the others, ask after you and have I any news. Have you won a medal yet. (That last is Griff's joke, not very funny perhaps, but then he's a bit dim, isn't he).

I took the kids to Poulton last week and Daniel was sick after going on the Big Wheel. By the way, I bought that jacket I told you about, remember? Much use it was hinting! You just pretended not to hear, but I've got it now anyway. Will keep it for your homecoming, whenever that's likely to be.

Remember me to the lads,

With love,

Sandra.

PS Mum asks to be remembered.

It told him nothing. Nothing. He wondered if the other men had letters like hers, brief, self-centred notes, adequate enough if you were twenty, thirty miles down the road, home at weekends, no bloody snipers just outside the door waiting to pick you off. Not enough for out here, ten hours flight and eight more in a truck, up to your ankles in stinking marsh mud, sweating, hungry, always fearful.

He closed his eyes, calling to mind the sweet-remembered moments of those last few days, her mother minding the children, bawdy, yelling so all the street could hear, 'Go on, Con! Give her something to remember you by!' and him driving the car, Sandra's car, down to the New Forest where they'd stayed all day and all night in the caravan, never seeing a sight of a fox or a deer, too busy in that small overheated, unsteady world of bed and coffee and egg-an'-chips to bother with the countryside around them.

She was no letter-writer, he knew that, but still he hoped that something, just a few words would creep in to let him know she too recalled a moment of that brief weekend. 'Mum asks to be remembered.' And that was all.

Dear Boy,

Got your letter today, and I must say I was surprised. Are you cross with your ever-loving? You sound very fed up but perhaps it's the war and everything. Honestly, I think about you all the time, and never miss the News on telly to see what you're doing. Only they haven't mentioned your lot yet. Are you actually in the war?

Of course, silly, I remember that weekend! We did have fun didn't we, though I do think we should have got out once or twice, seen something of the Forest while we were there. Mum still goes on about how good the kids were while we were away. Daniel's been playing up at school, but I told the Head he's missing his Dad which is near enough the truth! Not that he's all that civil when you're around. Griff called in last evening and gave Daniel a piece of his mind, said he ought to behave while his Dad's away. You can guess the reply to that! 'Con's not my Dad!' he said and Griff gave him a clip round the ear to help him mind what he says and where.

Sorry to hear about your poor feet. They say on the telly you're to have new boots, all of you. Something about the old ones not being made for jungle war. Typical!

I start my new job on Monday. Same office but working for Mr Morrison which will be nice. I've had a blond rinse since you went and Mr Morrison says it makes me look like a real secretary. 'If only she could type!' he says, which makes me laugh, because as you well know, I can! Type, that is.

With love,

Yours, Sandra.

PS It's definitely NOT three weeks since I last wrote. There must have been a mix-up in the post. Will make enquiries this end.

They'd been out on patrol all day, him and the rest of the Company, including young Berry, a boy doing a man's job if ever there was one, but doing his best to hide the fact that he was terrified.

'Try not to think about it,' Con told him. 'Tell yourself it's just another exercise, that's all. And for God's sake keep your voice down! The whole point of this game is to take them by surprise, get it?'

'Got it, Sarge.'

'Good lad.' There was no point in saying anything more, no point in trying to convince the boy that the rest of us, old hands, don't give a toss. Because he knows we're just as frightened as he is.

'Got a girl friend?' I asked and Berry nodded.

'Lives in Sheffield.' He smiled with secret pleasure. 'She writes me every day, well almost.'

'That's nice. You're lucky.'

'How about you, Sarge. Have you got a girl?'

Con considered the question. 'Yes, sort of. She doesn't write every day, though.'

Dear Boy,

I'm sending you some food etc. to remind you of home (no take-away, more's the pity!). The kids wanted to send chocolate, but I said it would melt on the journey, so they're sending you after-shave instead. Hope this is acceptable. The photo of me was taken a couple of weeks ago. Sexy, eh?

Now then. I had a visit from your sister if you can believe it, ticking me – us – off right roundly for nipping off to the New Forest like that. As if it's anything to do with her! She says it's all very well chucking the kids off onto my mother, but what about if You Know Who gets to hear about it? She may like to pretend I don't even exist, but she's only to have a quiet word with the kids and then...! Maybe we should move away, start again somewhere fresh, forget all about Ruby, what do you say? One of these days, my love, you're going to have to choose between us, I'm telling you straight.

Must rush. Going out tonight (do I hear you say, 'What, again?' Well, actually yes!)

Love, Sandra

They'd lost another two men last night. No gunfire, not a sound, just the two bodies thrown into the bushes where they fell. Knifed.

Young Berry had taken it better than he, Con had expected, not throwing up till much later, probably when he'd had time and opportunity to think about it. All those people back home, Mums, Dads, brothers, aunts and uncles, all grieving for their loss, and such a silly, useless war.

He'd found Berry, face down in the rough buran grass that surrounded the camp. 'Poor, miserable bloody people,' he was sobbing. 'They didn't want their kids to go in the first place. They weren't proper soldiers. They were just kids, ought to be in college, not in a war like this... ' He was thumping the ground with his fists like a petulant child, too distressed to know or care who heard him.

'Shut up, Berry,' Con said quietly. 'There's nothing you can do about it. They're gone, finished. Nothing, d'you understand?'

Slowly the boy rolled over and looked up, surprised to see Con leaning over him, embarrassed by the violence of his outburst. He struggled to get to his feet but Con held out a hand to stop him.

'Take your time,' he said, then after a moment, 'You'll be better now, you'll see.' He had a sudden impulse to take the boy in his arms, comfort him, rock him to sleep as someone had once done for him.

It had been snowing, he remembered, wet, cold snow that seeped through the inadequate uniform to freeze the very life from you in a matter of hours. One of the search party had found him, lain down beside him, close and caring, breathing warm, living air into him, and he could still recall the smell of the man, the feel of his arms around him, and his love for the stranger he would probably never see again.

'Sergeant....'

'Time to go,' Con said brusquely. 'The worst is over, believe me.'

'Yeah. Yeah, sure.' Berry sat up, rubbed at his tears with the sleeve of his shirt. Then he laughed. 'What a fool !'

'No.'

'I'm sorry.'

Con nodded. He knew what the boy had been through and was glad he hadn't given way to that sudden impulse, knowing that Berry was man enough to resent such a physical show of sympathy.

'Best take a walk before you go back to quarters, O.K.?'

'Yeah, O.K., Sergeant. And thanks.'

He'd seen a bird yesterday, brilliant green with a long, blue-black tail that feathered out almost like a peacock. They'd come upon each other, face to face on a broad, well-worn track, the bird surprised and cautious, Con speechless before such beauty. He'd stopped in his tracks, silent, one foot almost off the ground, and he smiled to see that the bird, too, was caught in mid-stride, its pale ivory foot drawn elegantly to its chest, the claws pink and manicured as a woman's. There was a moment when he could have sworn they understood the unreality of their situation, the bird a thing of the jungle, he, Sergeant First Class C.J. Rayner, a foreigner in every possible sense of the word.

'Hullo, bird,' he whispered, smiling, and told himself the creature responded, unafraid, with a soft whistling at the base of its throat, but it was imagination, the wish exaggerated in his mind so that he laughed at his absurdity.

He was conscious of cramp threatening to attack the muscle of his leg and unthinking, he stamped his foot on the ground. In a single flash of colour, the bird turned to lose itself in the rampant undergrowth and the moment was gone.

The episode had saddened him. He'd wanted to gather the bird to him, keep it for its exotic colour in the face of such waste all about him. He would tell Sandra about it in his next letter, carefully choosing the words he would use to describe it and knowing that she wouldn't have the faintest idea what he was trying to say.

... I showed Daniel the bit about the bird and he said, 'were you one over the eight? Funny aren't they, kids?' We all laughed.

Della cries because you're away so long, but I tell her you'll be back in time for her sixth birthday. You will, won't you? By the way, (talking of presents!) Griff arrived last night with a really nice reclining chair for the garden, said it 'fell off a lorry'! I said of course I couldn't accept it, but he insisted, said it was for the kids as well as me. Honestly, love, it's not as if it's something personal, you know what I mean? So you don't mind, do you. I mean, it's all very above board!

I meant to tell you, a Mrs Braseby has come to work in Mr Morrison's office, in the same room as me and it turns out she's a friend of Ruby's! Seems I can't get away from that woman. Anyway, we get on quite well, Mrs B. and me, but it's ever so difficult keeping my mouth shut. Apparently Ruby gets herself in quite a state, according to Mrs B., because (get this!) 'her partner is a soldier out there and she can't sleep for worrying about him, what with all that fighting and men getting killed'. Poor bitch, I could almost be sorry for her.

Love etc.

Sandra

It seemed unlikely that Ruby would let things get her down that easily. She was such a little thing, shy and anxious to please, but she had a good solid core to her, a streak of obstinacy that would prevent her going to pieces whatever happened. Con smiled to himself, remembering how she'd flown at him that time he'd called her 'Sandra' by mistake, forgiving him next day but making it plain he'd better mind out in future. Even if he were to get hurt, killed perhaps, still Ruby would be there, coping. Sandra must have got it wrong. Or that Mrs Braseby of hers.

Dear Con,

Whatever silly ideas are going on in your head? About me and Griff, I mean. I know he's not really a friend of yours, but he does know Mike and Tel and Jim Thorp and they're all friends of yours, aren't they? And it's only a bit of secondhand old garden furniture, so where's the harm, I say. But I'll send it back if you're going to make a fuss about it.

Anyway, to get to more serious matters, have you thought any more about us? U S, in big letters, you and me? Because my Mum says aren't I wasting my time, just writing letters and you away so much of the time when there's Daniel and Della to think about. Well actually, Con, I've been to see a solicitor, and he says quite right, this matter needs to be cleared up once and for all. You can't have it all your own way, you know, and the kids need a father, specially Daniel, and his birth-Dad (is that the right word?) is playing up again, talking about 'child allowances' and 'access time'. He's got his solicitor on the job, talking about 'moral climate' and suchlike, pointing at the photo of the kids on the bookcase. So watch out! I think things may be coming to a head. Well, anyway, have a think and let me know.

Yours, Sandra

He had a copy of that photograph in his wallet, the two children on the beach that brilliant summer's day, the tearaway Daniel, an unlovable child, raw, raucous, an unattractive, runny-nosed urchin. And Della, sweet Della, as different from her brother (or indeed, her mother) as it was possible for any child to be. Whatever became of his life, he would always feel deprived were she to be taken from him.

Berry said, 'Last night in this dump, Sarge!'

'That's right.'

'Me an' the lads are going into town. Will you be coming?'

'Yeah, maybe.'

Berry winked. 'Find us some girls, eh?'

'Why not.' Berry had grown up in the five months they'd been here, lost his innocence, become a grown man. Like all the rest of them.

'See you then, Sarge. In about half an hour?'

'Yes. O.K.'

There were only four weeks to go before they all got out of this mess, on the way back home again. He hoped Berry wouldn't get killed in the meantime. Not with that girl of his in Sheffield, writing to him every day, waiting for him.

Dear Con,

You've been having a right old time on leave by the sound of it. And you complain about me having the odd night out.

Something has come up. Eileen (Mrs Braseby in the office to you) says she'd been chatting to, guess who, Ruby and says now she's really got herself worked up, nothing to do with the war, she's got the idea her soldier-boy was having it off with another woman before he went overseas. She'd suspected all along (so she says) but now she's determined to find out who the woman is. Eileen says, will I go and see Ruby and have a talk with her, calm her down. Why me, I wanted to know, and she said, because I look the sort of person who knows about these things, people having affairs and that! What a cheek. I think she (Eileen) is suspicious because, as she sees it, Ruby and me have a lot in common, i.e. our men out there fighting the war, both from this town, both Sergeants etc., and I think maybe she's not as stupid as she looks. Anyway, who would be the likely person to put such an idea into Ruby's head, I wonder, unless your sister has been busy again. Honestly, Con, I do wish you'd write and tell her to keep her nose out of things.

XXX Sandra

Wasn't it enough that his boots were still leaking, that the monsoon would start any day, and that four of the men were down with something very like malaria. Now they were to be blessed with a new young subaltern, so fresh out from the UK that he still had creases in his trousers.

'Makes you puke, Sarge, these young guys. Don't know a thing about war - or about anything else, for that matter.' Berry talking, the old hand, the survivor of, how many, ten, fifteen night attacks? Something like that - you gave up counting in the end.

'He'll learn.'

'Yeah, I guess so.'

Con said, 'How's the girlfriend these days?', smiling to see a suspicion of a blush on Berry's cheeks.

'She's expecting,' the boy said, looking pleased. 'Any day now.'

'Well done.'

'We didn't plan it.'

'Pity you didn't wait, then. Till you got home.'

'She'll manage. Whatever happens. She's a soft little thing, you'd never guess it but she's really tough, deep down.' Berry smiled, confident that all would be well. 'She'll manage,' he said. 'Whatever.'

Con,

You're always ticking me off about something these days. Yes, I know we agreed not to talk about Ruby any more, but it's very difficult knowing I could bump into her any day. What would I say to her, I'd like to know. And it's no good asking you because you just get ratty about it. Is the war getting to you? Because if it is perhaps you'd be interested to know that sitting here waiting for you is not a load of fun either. I mean, I'm still young enough to like pretty clothes and dancing and that, but what's the point with no one to notice you, only two noisy kids and their bloody father only a few streets away. And now you, Con, keeping on getting on at me.

Perhaps I shouldn't have told you about Mrs Braseby and Ruby being friends, but I thought you'd want to know. In any case, the sooner you get back and we can sort all this out, the better. It's not easy for me, either, you know.

The kids and me have been invited to Cornwall for a week. It'll be lovely down there this time of year. You're not going to grumble, I hope. It's about the only holiday I shall get with you away...

He didn't bother to read the rest.

He stubbed out his cigarette and let the single sheet of notepaper slip to the ground. He felt immeasurably tired, not only of war and all its discomforts, but already weary of the days, weeks ahead, of the common, day-to-day problems with bills and mortgages and plumbers, household rows and commuting to work, and suddenly war didn't seem so awful as a way of life. At least one avoided the complications of women.

Tomorrow they were off again into the jungle, for the last time before they handed over to B Company. At least, so the word had gone round, but you couldn't be sure of anything and it was just as likely that that smart, new, know-it-all subaltern would volunteer them for some dam' silly escapade and some, maybe all of those bright young lads who'd been at his side for the past five months, maybe at this very last minute they would go and get themselves killed. Maybe he too would not survive?

He was glad that young Berry had had no intention of going into town to 'find a couple of women', no more than he had himself. It would have spoiled the picture he had of the man, so childishly pleased with the photograph of the girlfriend and the new baby.

'You got any children, Sarge?'

'No.'

'For choice?'

'God no!' He'd have given anything for a little girl like Della. 'No, it just never happened.'

'I'm sorry for you. No, really, I'm sorry!'

Con smiled. 'Thank you. But there's no need. We're used to the idea now.'

Someone shouted 'Mail van leaving!' and through the flap of his tent he could see the men hurrying to the Admin Tent, envelopes in hand, last-minute notes finished off with a message of undying love and a promise to return home soon.

Well, he'd finally made up his mind. He'd take no more of her mindless chatter, her nagging, her flaunted infidelities, most of all, her total inability to sense even one hundredth of his desperate need to be comforted in this terrible, enervating, death-ridden jungle of a country a million miles from anywhere. He'd tried to tell her, written more letters in those few months than he had written in a whole lifetime, begging her to feel something of what he suffered, to read into his words something of what was going on in his mind. While she, she wrote of parties and new clothes, made trouble between him and his sister, even more so between him and Ruby. Very well, if she was bent on mischief, he would let her know just where it had brought them.

There was still time to get a letter in the post and with no further hesitation, he took out his pen and started to write.

Dear Sandra,

I've decided. I'm going back to my wife, if she'll have me...

ADJUDICATION

This excellent, timely and intriguing story describes the reaction of Con, a sergeant in the army, to the letters sent to him by his self-absorbed partner while he is on active service during the war and his reactions to them.

Written in the third person, this story utilises the technique of a series of letters which progresses the plot line and develops the foibles of the characters in a manner which keeps the reader's interest.

Noted particularly is the self-assured, self-confident voice of a practised author. The detail in describing the encounter with the bird is excellent: 'He smiled to see that the bird, too, was caught in mid-stride, its pale ivory foot drawn elegantly to its chest, the claws pink and manicured as a woman's.' However, earlier in the story the reader needs to know that the setting is an army camp, not a hospital or a prison.

To improve its marketability, edit the opening paragraph carefully, making each word pay its way. Leave our unnecessary words and avoid run-on sentences using 'so' and 'and'.

The dénouement should tie up the loose ends of the story. We need to know if the entire company went home safely, especially Barry.

A worthy winner. Congratulations.

Pat King

A Page of Prose Competition

Sponsor:

Hodder & Stoughton Publishers

Adjudicators: Chandlers Ford Writers

WINNERS & HIGHLY COMMENDED

Competitors were invited to write a short story, including a coin, a face and a misunderstanding. One page only, 250 word maximum.

Winners

	Prize	Title	Author / *Pseudonym*
1st	**£50**	**The Dust of the Ground**	**Fiona Knight** *Hugh Briss*
2nd	**£30**	**Fall Guy**	**Pam Baddeley** *Dark Willow*
3rd	**£20**	**Flip Side**	**Lynne Pearson** *Maggie Lawrence*

Highly Commended

Title	Author	Pseudonym
Small Change	**Lynda Carr**	*Coralie Brook*
Reunited	**Sarah Way**	*Ben Benson.*
Living for the Past	**Brian Potter**	*George March*
Accidents Will Happen	**Pauline Morgan**	*Daubenton*
Untitled	**Gill James**	*Jude Jackson*
Twister	**Jayne Jenner**	*1 Lincoln*

THE DUST OF THE GROUND

FIONA KNIGHT

An Extract from the Journals of Dr James Grieve
Archaeological Season 1922-1923
Noqdi, Persia

Noqdi. Wednesday, 17th January 1923

The argument continued. I was desperate to try our fortune at the Sumerian gold mines of Havilah, but the Professor insisted that we complete this fruitless dig. Exasperated, we tossed the gold sovereign; as it tumbled into the dust of the ground I called "tails", but instead of St. George, I was looking at King George's head.

Noqdi. Thursday, 18th January 1923

It took Hiddekel's strongest men an eternity to excavate the massive fossilized tree, below which was created a rough tomb. Three sets of remains were discovered at this stratum below the barren desert, and the earlier deposits from the lush vegetation, rich in exotic fruits. A human male was the first to be uncovered, beside which lay the remains of a human female, both ancient skeletons being complete, with the minor exception of one rib missing from the man. Without doubt, the cause of both deaths was a tremendous fall from a great height. Not a single artefact was to be found, but close to the woman lay a skeleton of a large serpent, genus unknown.

So still the only gold in this God-forsaken wilderness is the Professor's traitorous sovereign. It is beyond understanding. Last year Carnarvon and Carter achieved the archaeological zenith that is Tut-ankh-Amen. Our nadir is a petrified tree and a couple of worthless, unidentifiable snake eaters, of who knows what genesis?

Adjudication

Congratulations! This is exceptional. A mile ahead of any other entry we judged. A page of prose of which any writer would be proud. Very enjoyable.

	Very ***Good***	***Average***	***Weak***
Originality/Use of words	✓		
Dialogue			
Narrative	✓		
Pace/Apt ending	✓		
Presentation	✓		

Chandlers Ford Writers

Feature Article Competition

Sponsor:

Southern Daily Echo

Writing Excellence is Our Business

Adjudicator: David Brine

WINNERS & HIGHLY COMMENDED

*Competitors were invited to send a 450 word feature article on all, or any, of the following subjects: **1. Olympic Games 2. D-Day 3. Leap Year***

Winners

	Prize	Title	Author / *Pseudonym*
1st	£150 & Echo trophy	Shaking Hands in Berlin	James Prickett *Sprinter*
2nd	£100	Olympic Games	Pauline Morgan *Daubenton*
3rd	£75	The Invasion of Hampshire D-Day	Malcolm Welshman *A Page*

Highly Commended

Title	Author	Pseudonym
In Step	Lesley Drew	*Henry Nein*
The G I Wall in Southampton	N. Bradshaw	*Fran Millington*
What Price Olympic Glory?	Janette Brown	*Emily Brown*
Leap Year Day Customs Act	Betty Hill	*Pat Samby*

SHAKING HANDS IN BERLIN

JAMES PRICKETT

The slight figure crouched, gouging out a couple of holes with a trowel. He scooped out a small pile of cinders, smoothing round the edges of the holes with his fingers. Fragments of grit clung to his skin. Ever since he'd arrived, everyone had wanted to shake his hand.

The country boy from Alabama, after nine days at sea on the Atlantic, smiled to himself. He imagined he was about to run 'over a ground of burning fire', as his father put it.

'Auf die Plätze.'

He slid his feet into the holes he'd dug. He splayed his fingers just behind the white start line. Over 100,000 Germans were chanting: 'Jesse Owens! Jesse Owens!'

Up in the grandstand, in the box reserved for the guest of honour, The Führer looked on. The feverish adulation of one man, a foreigner, and a black American at that, must have struck him.

'Fertig.'

The crowd had eyes for only one figure, the slight, long-legged sprinter, primed on all fours, waiting for the gun.

With him on the track was the German, Erich Borchmeyer. In 1932, Borchmeyer had run against the schoolboy Owens in Los Angeles. Owens had won, and Borchmeyer had asked Jesse for a signed photo. Four years on, the German champion greeted Jesse in Berlin with a handshake and the words, 'I still have that photo. One day I shall show my children.'

The gun fired. The final of the 100 metres was underway, and Jesse Owens' feet were about to carry him into history.

'Those Americans should be ashamed of themselves for letting their medals be won by a Neger,' Hitler apparently said. 'I would never shake the hand of one.'

Owens brushed off Hitler's rebuff with the comment, 'I didn't come here to shake hands anyway.'

Two days later, in the long jump, the blue-eyed blond Lutz Long embraced Jesse. Owens had just set a new Olympic record with a massive jump of 26 feet and 5 inches to claim his second gold.

In his final scheduled event, the 200 metres, Owens set a world record time of 20.7 seconds to create a hat-trick of gold.

Owens was not due to run in the relay team. Stoller and Glickman, two Jewish sprinters, were mysteriously dropped by the American coaches. Owens protested that his team mates should run. But the coaches insisted Owens did as he was told: Owens ran. His fourth, unprecedented gold resulted.

Thousands mobbed him, managed to touch him, clap him on the back, shake his hand. Yes. Jesse Owens did shake hands in Berlin.

Adjudication

Congratulations. It is rare to read a piece of writing that sheds new light on a well known story. While your article didn't tell me anything new factually, it made me look at the Jesse Owens story in a different way. It was a brave choice of subject. You pulled it off exceptionally well and were a deserved winner. Quite simply it was a gripping and beautifully written account. It starts intriguingly - you don't immediately reveal the ending. I wanted to carry on reading and I liked the way you revealed more and more until I was certain that I knew it was going to be about the 1936 Olympics. The article is well-paced and maintains its impetus right up until the neat finish. I hesitate to say this about any piece of writing but I'm not sure this could be improved.

David Brine

Writing For Children Competition

Sponsor:

Little Tiger Press

Adjudicator: Jude Evans

WINNERS & HIGHLY COMMENDED

Competitors were invited to submit the 500 opening words of a work for children and a synopsis of the remainder, either fiction or non-fiction or alternatively up to three pages of poetry or light verse. Entries stated the intended age range: 4-7, 8-11 or 12 and over.

Winners

AGE 4-7	PRIZE	TITLE	AUTHOR / *PSEUDONYM*
2nd joint	**Book prizes**	**My Mum's a Secret Agent**	**Ann Wright** *Ann Bear*
2nd	**Book prizes**	**Dial A for Angel**	**Giselle Finn** *Bag End*

Highly Commended

TITLE	AUTHOR	PSEUDONYM
Foxes Play Swapsies	**Sheila Black**	*Fatso*

The standard of entries for the three categories of this competition were particularly high and made judging a difficult, but pleasurable, task.

Entrants should not be discouraged if they were not among the prizewinners because the judging was very close indeed.

MY MUM'S A SECRET AGENT

ANN WRIGHT

A Story for 4-7 Year Olds

My Mum's a secret agent. I've suspected it for a long time – well, all of this week.

But when I told my friends at school today, they laughed. They said it was just another wacky idea of mine. 'Prove it,' they said. So I will.

Finding proof would be easy if I could get into the cupboard under the stairs. Mum locks her spy equipment in this cupboard. Last night I heard strange noises, like someone moaning, coming from it. Mum probably caught a baddie, tied him up and left him in there until M15 can take him away. If only I could find the key.

Mum says she works in a boring office. She never mentions her job or the people she works with. It's obvious she does something secret. Sometimes she goes away for several days. She's always exhausted when she comes home, too tired to tell us where she went. Of course, she wouldn't be allowed to tell anyone the details of her missions.

She doesn't wear clothes for her office job either. I've never seen her in a skirt, only trousers. While my friends's Mum wears smart shoes with heels, Mum's are like trainers. This means she can run fast to catch the bad guys or make a quick getaway.

I need to find some of her gadgets to show my friends.

Mum's diary. I'm sure Mum's diary has secret codes written inside. She keeps it in a locked box in a locked drawer by her bed. I picked the lock of the drawer with one of Mum's hair pins (must be why she wears them). The lock on the box was harder, made so spies can't open it. I was searching for a smaller pick when Mum came into the room. She was really upset with me. The diary must contain very important information.

Mum's ring. I've noticed Mum's ring shines brightly every now and then. she disappears every time it gleams. This must be a signal to contact base. It's a shame I can't look at the ring. She never takes it off her finger.

Mum's earrings. Mum always wears the same long, dangly earrings to work. The big stone in each one must be a camera lens so M15 can monitor Mum's missions. I tried to dig out one of the stones but they wouldn't budge. I hope I didn't scratch the lens.

Mum's watch. This isn't a stylish ladies watch. It's big and practical with lots of buttons. I think these buttons activate a laser beam to cut through metal. I had her watch in pieces looking through the bits inside, when she caught me. She went mad.

'Josh,' she screamed, 'what's got into you?' I left the room quickly.

Mum's handbag. I've borrowed Mum's handbag while she's cooking tea. There must be a gadget or two in here. She thinks I'm in my room doing my homework – well, this is homework of sorts.

Josh, 8 years, private eye

Synopsis

My Mum's a Secret Agent is 1235 words in length and is intended for 4-7 year olds.

Eight year old Josh thinks his Mum is brilliant and she cannot lead the boring life she appears to. His latest theory is that she is a secret agent and his school friends laugh at his idea. So he sets out to prove she is.

Under the stairs is a cupboard, which is always locked. In here, Josh is sure his mother keeps all her spy equipment. He need to find the keys to the cupboard and searches through his mother's room and handbag. All the items he finds, mobile phone, pen, watch, brooch, sunglasses – he takes them apart thinking they are spy gadgets, destroying them in the process. He is nearly caught with red lipstick smudged on his bed.

To his delight he finds the keys and keeps them to look in the cupboard later on. After tea when his mum starts to find her broken belongings, Josh decides to hide in the cupboard.

To his surprise, brooms, pots and the missing cat fall on him when he opens the door. Now he has a new theory. His Mum's a witch.

Adjudication

This is a really strong, fun idea for an early reader, with a great twist at the end! The writing style is similarly strong – we get a lovely sense of this determined child's voice and character. The story begins with an opening paragraph that really draws you in, funny, spare and direct. The child's perspective sings out to us and we can't resist the hook that we are thrown.

The author has laid out the story very clearly and there's an attractive simplicity to the plot. The secret agent idea is a great one, particularly for pulling in boy readers.

Having said this, there is still much that could be developed within this narrative framework. The telling could be sparkier – this age group love excitement and surprises, so Josh's discoveries and his developing convictions could be heightened. The tension when he's taking his Mum's things apart and his Mum's eventual discovery could all be stepped up and developed with more fun and drama. The writing would certainly benefit from more dialogue. At the moment it's a little isolated with mainly just Josh in the picture. Perhaps we could see him interact with Mum more? It would be good to see more of Mum's exasperation and the humour this would offer. The story might also benefit from more of a break-up in the time span. Perhaps we could go through the week mentioned in the first paragraph?

If lifted and sharpened, My Mum's a Secret Agent has great potential. It's a brilliant title and concept and could be a delight to read.

Jude Evans

DIAL A FOR ANGELS

GISELLE FINN

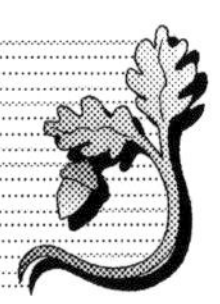

A Story for 4-7 Year Olds

I saw the mobile phone at the school jumble sale. I had always wanted one but Mum said it turns kids' brains into custard. My big brother has got one but his brains are already custard.

I had to show the phone to my best friend.

'Zoë!' I called out.

'Here I am, Chloë,' she said from right behind me.

She was always doing that, appearing from nowhere. But angels do that sort of thing.

'Look what I've found,' I said, holding up my brilliant discovery.

Amazingly she didn't look pleased at all. She looked really scared.

'Put it back,' she snapped, 'It's rubbish.'

I was too upset to argue, I mean, angels aren't supposed to talk like that. So I put the phone back in the basket and walked away. However, something made me turn around and look back. I was just in time to see a terrible thing.

Zoë stuffed the phone into her bag.

I ran back to her.

'What's in your bag?' I asked.

'Nothing!' she said.

I was heart-broken. Zoë was lying, and there was one thing I was sure of...angels don't lie.

'Are you playing a game?' I asked.

'No,' said Zoë. 'Why?'

You said the phone was rubbish, so why have you bought it?'

'I haven't.'

'Yes you have,' I said. I saw you put it into your bag.'

'No, I didn't!'

Her eyes were as big as cow's eyes. She almost made me believe her.

'I saw you,' I whispered.

Oh don't make such a fuss, Chloë,' said Zoë. 'It's only a silly toy phone.'

I wanted to cry. I really had believed that Zoë was the best friend I had always dreamed of.

Suddenly I couldn't hold back the tears any longer. I turned and ran. I had no idea where I would go. I couldn't see Mum anywhere. I dashed into the girls' cloakroom. Luckily there was no-one in there. I flung myself into a cubicle, slammed the door closed, locked it and burst into silent tears.

I wished I had Charlie Croc with me. Charlie Croc was my favourite toy, except that he was much more than a toy to me. He was a soft, green crocodile with a lovely smile. But it was his eyes that were the thing. They seemed so real. When I looked into them I always knew that I could trust him with anything.

Mum always made me leave him at home in case he got lost. I knew she was right, but I badly needed him now. I had really believed that Zoë was the best friend I had wanted for so long. One I could share secrets with, one who would always be on my side and would always be my partner when we had to go in pairs.

Not one who would lie to me.

I had to know what was going on. Somehow I had to get hold of that phone.

Synopsis

Chapter One

At an after-school jumble sale, Chloë spots a strange mobile phone and shows it to Zoë who tells her it is rubbish. When Zoë sneaks the phone into her bag and denies having done so, Chloë is forced to admit that her 'angel' is a liar. She is determined to get to the heart of the matter.

Chapter Two

At a football practice Chloë sneaks into Zoë's bag and takes the phone. Zoë begs Chloë not to use it and especially not to press the sparkly pink button. Chloë presses it.

Chapter Three

The girls sway in the whirling lights, the phone rings, a tinkling, enticing sound. Chloë answers it and hears a voice asking her who she wants to communicate with. Chloë says she wants to understand how an angel can lie. The voice tells her to dial A for Angel. Zoë tries to stop her but it is too late. When the lights fade back to normal, the two girls have swapped bodies.

Chapter Four

Chloë is then teased by other kids who think she's Zoë. Chloë realizes she didn't know about this teasing. She has been a poor friend. She has an unhappy time and wants her real home, real Mum and Charlie Croc.

Chapter Five

She knows her only hope of swapping back is to find the phone. She runs back to the cloakrooms but it's not there. Eventually she finds it in the teacher's drawer. She then catches up with Zoë and tells her she is sorry she hasn't been much of a true friend and she cannot live a lie a moment longer.

Chapter Six

They find a private place and press the sparkly button. They swap back. Zoë agrees to tell no more lies and Chloë agrees to 'communicate' better with her friend.

Adjudication

There is some fantastic writing in the sample pages for Dial A for Angel; tight, pacy, direct, funny, and with a real emotional pull. The first few lines in particular are lovely; effortless with humour, the author manages to set up Chloë's character, her relationship with her brother and mother, introduces us to Chloë's angel and draw us right into the story, quite an achievement!
The dialogue is strong and convincing and Chloë's need for her special friend is going to ring true for all children. The author has very convincingly captured the intensity of the girls' relationships and emotions.
The synopsis shows lots of promise, too. The idea of swapping bodies is full of potential. A story about an angel friend could likewise be magical for young girls. Both of these themes offer a rich vein of narrative opportunity. However, at the moment the story does not quite get the most out of these themes. Zoë doesn't seem to have many magical, 'angelic' qualities and if she is not an angel this needs to be clearer to the reader and what it means to Zoë. It is never clear, for example, why Zoë does lie. Perhaps it would be an idea to show that she is teased before the swap. Surely Chloë would know that Zoë was teased, if she's her best friend?
Dial A for Angel is a great title and a strong idea. With re-working, this sparky, fun writing could make a magical early reader.

Jude Evans

WINNERS & HIGHLY COMMENDED

Competitors were invited to submit the 500 opening words of a work for children and a synopsis of the remainder, either fiction or non-fiction or alternatively up to three pages of poetry or light verse. Entries stated the intended age range: 4-7, 8-11 or 12 and over. Maximum length per entry 500 words.

Winners

Age 8-11	Prize	Title	Author / *Pseudonym*
1st	**Book prizes**	**Tomb Raiders**	**Giselle Finn** *Bag End*
2nd	**Book prizes**	**The Long Road**	**Jan Lee** *Emanoel*

Highly Commended

Title	Author	Pseudonym
Family Secrets	**Evelyn Harris**	*Chris Lewis*
The Secret of Whale Island	**Brian Lux**	*Black Fox*
Granny Liz	**Susan K Franklin**	*Ben Ali*

TOMB RAIDER

GISELLE FINN

A Story for 8-11 Year Olds

'Have you heard the awful news?'

'Don't tell me,' said Gilly, my best friend. 'We've got to go to the after school club again?'

'Got it in one,' I replied.

'At least we get chocolate biscuits I suppose,' she sighed.

'Yeah,' I said. 'We also get Caravan Man AND we have to watch one of his 'interesting fillums'.

Gilly threw her rucksack on the floor and collapsed dramatically on top pretending to sob. I knew how she felt.

Caravan Man is our form teacher. His real name is Mr. Dougall. He is Irish, which is why he says 'fillums rather than films; he is bonkers about history; and he is criminally insane.

We call him Caravan Man because he drives to school with his caravan in tow and parks the lot in the school car park.

Apart from that, he's fine...not.

Gilly and I dawdled into the assembly hall where the after school care club was held. At least we could get ahead of the run on chocolate biscuits.

I hate the assembly hall. Mostly because it smells of dust and sweaty bodies as we do P.E. in there as well. Two other kids from our class had arrived already: Eddie Jackson, a boring boff and Josh Carter, who was okay but a bit quiet.

There were no chocolate biscuits. It surely couldn't get any worse.

'Hello, Katy,' said Eddie, the boff, bounding over to me. 'Are you going to the after school club too?'

'Yes, worst luck,' I said.

'Don't worry,' he said, 'Caravan Man says we're watching a film on ancient Egypt.'

'Really? I don't think I can cope with the excitement,' I said in my flattest voice.

'I don't believe it,' said Gilly. 'We're stuck in school with a boring boring teacher, watching a boring film and with only boring biscuits to eat.'

'Anyway,' said Eddie. 'Caravan Man has asked if we'll go and help him bring his stuff from the caravan.'

'I wonder what stuff,' said Gilly

'His stamp collection, probably,' I mumbled.

'No,' said Josh. He said it was a DVD player with a seriously huge screen.'

'Really' said Gilly, her huge, blue eyes becoming even huger. 'Let's go.'

The four of us went outside into the freezing cold playground to help Caravan Man unload all this supposedly exciting stuff.

'It's freezing out here,' said Gilly shivering and rubbing her upper arms with her hands.

'Never mind,' said Eddie. 'We can go and lose ourselves in the nice hot sunshine of ancient Egypt.'

Gilly and I whirled our forefingers around in a circular motion just above our ears. Indicating, that this was the final proof that Eddie, the boff, was indeed a demented nutter.

Unfortunately he turned just in time to see us do it.

'Just teasing,' I said.

'Sure you were, ' he replied looking at me as if I had bird poo on my nose.

This day was going from bad to very much worse.

Synopsis

Kate, Gilly, Eddie and Josh are hacked off at having to go to an afterschool film club to watch a 'boring' film on ancient Egypt.

However, things look up when it turns out that they are to view the film on a giant plasma screen. When Eddie 'disappears' into the screen and becomes part of the Egyptian drama, Kate and the others must find the courage to dive into the plasma miasma and save him from the awesome tomb robbers.

Once there, they must devise a plan to save the treasure buried in the heart of a huge pyramid. First they must find their way past lairs and traps in the corridors and galleries of the pyramid, after which, will they find their way back to their chilly classroom?

The story is a form of 'time-slip' though in fact, going through the plasma screen takes the children into a drama of the DVD and the idea could thus lend itself to 'space-slip', 'geography-slip' and so on. Further possibilities are therefore limitless.

ADJUDICATION

Tomb Raiders has a freshness and sparkle in the writing that really stood out when reading the entries to this competition. A deserving winner, the sample has a great sense of character, a bubbly humour and narrative voice that is gently quirky, charming and most importantly, utterly convincing. In the idle natter of Gilly and Kate, Bag End quickly establishes many things: scene; (I hate the assembly hall. Mostly because it smells of dust and sweaty bodies,) atmosphere; (Gilly threw her rucksack on the floor and collapsed dramatically on top of it pretending to sob. I knew how she felt) and very quickly, the dynamic of the main characters, Gilly and Kate's easy friendship, the more awkward interaction with Eddie, the boff, and as yet very little of Josh Carter (who was okay but a bit quiet).

The tone of the narrative is very strong, the atmosphere that of a very ordinary school afternoon, dull, dull, dull. Setting it up to be completely turned upside down when the four enter the strange Egyptian world of the plasma screen.

The fantasy adventure of this story is not given in huge detail in the synopsis and would need to be carefully thought through to be watertight. However, the lightness of touch the author brings and the potential of light and shade, tension and humour, the drama of the developing relationships between the friends and the incongruity of their modern day attitudes in the ancient location, hold great potential. Tomb Raiders (great title) could be a real romp of a read to delight young readers.

Jude Evans

WINNERS & HIGHLY COMMENDED

Competitors were invited to submit the 500 opening words of a work for children and a synopsis of the remainder, either fiction or non-fiction or alternatively up to three pages of poetry or light verse. Entries stated the intended age range: 4-7, 8-11 or 12 and over. Maximum length per entry 500 words.

Winners

AGE 12+	PRIZE	TITLE	AUTHOR / *PSEUDONYM*
1st	**Book prizes**	**The Baker Street Irregular**	**Linda Downing** *C D Devereux*
2nd	**Book prizes**	**Under King**	**Evelyn Harris** *Chris Lewis*

Highly Commended

TITLE	AUTHOR	PSEUDONYM
Felix Detective	**Hermione Laake**	*Becky Orange*
The Wrath of God	**Giselle Finn**	*Bag End*
The Eorls School	**David Caldo**	*Black Wizard*

BAKER STREET IRREGULARS

Linda Downing

A story for 12+ year olds

Cauley stank, not the gentle whiff of someone who hasn't washed for a few days, but an eye-watering blend of dark cellars, ancient meals, greasy clothes and sweaty night. Fighting against all of these other smells and winning by a nose was the stench of Thames mud that clung to every pore of Cauley's grey skin. Black and richly filthy, the mud oozed around his bare feet as Cauley peered down looking intently for anything that could be dug up, cleaned up and sold.

A freezing cold wind whipped by and nipped his nose and a thin, icy drizzle soaked his ragged clothes. Cauley began to snivel with disappointment and hunger. All of the other mudlarks who made a thin sort of living dredging the banks of London's great river had given up for the day, only Cauley remained, kept there by desperation and an empty belly. He hopped from one freezing foot to another and with his tatty clothes flapping in the wind, Cauley looked like nothing so much as a scrawny, scavenging bird.

"Stinking, lousy river, five hours and not a bleeding penny." He straightened his aching back and looked down river where dark clouds promised even more rain. If only he could find some shelter, he could carry on till dark. Scanning the river bank, his eyes fell on the rotting hull of an ancient rowing boat, perfect!

And so it was that, squatting down behind the boat's rotting timbers, Cauley was quite hidden from view when he saw the murder.

Cauley had known from the first that there was something terribly wrong. He'd been concentrating on retrieving what he thought might be a half penny when he heard the crunching scattering sounds of someone making their way down the shingle of the riverbank. Instinctively he'd crouched down further out of sight, peering through one of the gaps in the rotting wood. A man was trying to run down the stony bank, a task made all the more difficult because of his wooden leg. He stopped and looked behind him, then turned and looked about wildly as if searching for some place to hide, an expression of fear and fury on his tanned and weather-beaten face.

In the distance Cauley heard voices and the stranger heard them too for he stopped and reached twice into the pocket of his rough jacket, the first time bringing out a sharply pointed knife, the second time he produced a small leather purse which he looked at for a few short seconds before stretching his arm back and flinging it with all his might towards the dark waters of the Thames. Then the man turned, looked back towards the river bank, obviously waiting for the owners of these distant voices to appear. That he expected them to be dangerous was obvious from the way he squared his shoulders and set his feet firmly apart. Cauley heard the grate and crunch of shingle as the man's wooden leg ground down firmly into the stony sludge of the riverback.

The stranger did not have to wait long. Suddenly like two figures in some horrible puppet show, two men appeared, black silhouettes against a greying sky. For a few seconds everything seemed to go quiet. Cauley held his breath for fear that it might sound loud in that awful stillness.

Synopsis

It's been a bad day for Tom Cauley, a London mudlark, trying to make a living scavenging on the bank of the River Thames. Not only is he hungry and broke, he's just seen a man murdered.

Will Tom and his friend, the strangely silent Sludge Monkey, evade the clutches of the arch criminal, Moriarty? Will they be able to help Mr Sherlock Holmes solve the mystery of the kidnapped boy and a missing diamond?

Adjudication

The Baker Street Irregulars is a delightful piece of writing. This introduction to Cauley, and to the mystery of the kidnapped boy and the missing diamonds, is an excellent example of how to use 500 words to their best advantage.

From its first, hugely evocative sentence to the exquisite tension at the end of this extract, the writing is tight and effective. Rich in tone and atmosphere, the language evokes a strong sense of period and location. Even though the scene doesn't allow for much dialogue, Cauley's one line gives a great sense of character; "Stinking, lousy river, five hours and not a bleeding penny." His actions and motivations, his hunger, his desperation and his grit give us a real empathy with Cauley. By the second paragraph, we're hooked and we care. The extract is strong in drama, the narrative, pacy but smooth. What really made this piece stand out was its great execution of writing within a genre. It is unlikely to be a strikingly original story and the characters will have an element of stereotype to them- but this makes it no less strong: writing this good will always have much to give to children. The different elements of writing blend beautifully, so that setting, character, plot, drama, background details all sit together seamlessly. The reader absorbs all these things without even knowing it. It is a convincing start and we all want to read more! As a publisher, if we were to take on a project such as this, we'd have a few queries to discuss. The title needs to be much more exciting. The synopsis should have more detailed plotting. Using the character of Sherlock Holmes could be problematic; trying to recreate a much-loved and established literary figure in your own book could prove very tricky and might be a device best avoided. Much depends on how the novel develops whether this device will work or whether we'd be better creating a new detective character to interact with Cauley. However we see no insurmountable problems at this point and wish the author every success.

Jude Evans

Be a Successful Writer

VIEWPOINT

I was lucky enough to win the Poetry Competition. It was a wonderful day, the seminars were so inspiring and informing and Margaret Graham's workshop, The Structure of Your Novel is the Key to your Novel's Success was exceptional.

I was delighted to receive my Highly Commended certificate with my poetry entry. I am growing!

The day was a valuable opportunity for me to listen to and meet literary agents and to meet other writers. My one to one appointment with a literary agent was very promising. Subsequently I have sent it to her and am awaiting her response with great hope."

I came away with a good deal of thought-provoking stuff to mull over – as well as the trophy which is still safely in the box while I decide where to put it.

Childhood Between and During the Wars Competition

Sponsor:

AGE Concern

HAMPSHIRE

Adjudicator: Chris J. Perry

WINNERS & HIGHLY COMMENDED

Competitors were invited to submit autobiographical entries on the theme ***Childhood Before and During the Wars****, in prose or poetry. Illustrations, photographs, sketches and maps were welcomed. Maximum: 2000 words per entry. Winning manuscripts were eligible for publication in 'There's more to Life' (Age Concern Hampshire's Bi-monthly Newspaper) Registered Charity No. 290874.*

Winners

	Prize	Title	Author / *Pseudonym*
1st	**£50**	**The Christmas Carousel**	**Sarah Curling** *Anne Everest*
2nd	**£25**	**The Score Card**	**Richard Holdsworth** *St Leonards*
3rd	**£10**	**The First Air Raid**	**George Scholfield** *Golly Gee*

Highly Commended

Title	Author	Pseudonym
Time Warp	**Jenny Wren**	**Jen**

[Editor's note: The winning entry will be published in the autumn edition of Age Concern's publication, There's More to Life. The 1998 winning manuscript, Friday with Grandad, written by Mr L Moran was adapted by John Dunn, director of The Phoenix Theatre into a play which was performed at the AGM of Hampshire Age Concern. The 1999 winning entry was also produced in collaboration with Mr L Moran, as a short play linking bullying with childhood and with elderly people, the theme of the half-yearly meeting of Age Concern, Hampshire on 21st June 2000.]

THE CHRISTMAS CAROUSEL

SARAH CURLING

Late in 1941, when I was ten years old, I was taken by my mother to visit Mr Marks, a tailor with a shop in the town centre. Mother needed some fabric to lengthen my school tunic. Clothes and material were scarce and strictly rationed. At the time it had become quite usual to have a band of similar or even contrasting colour inserted just above the hem.

When our mission was explained, the tailor went to a cupboard and without comment handed a brown paper parcel to my mother. When she opened it, we found that it contained not the hideously clashing fabric that I was dreading, but what appeared to be a brand new navy gymslip and also a matching coat. They fitted me perfectly.

'Take them, take them, my dear,' the tailor addressed me kindly and then whispered to my mother as she offered to pay. His wife came out from behind the workshop and also handed me a box which l later found contained a Christmas Carousel – a delicate structure of wood with beautifully carved figures arranged on three turntables, one above the other. From that time it became part of our annual Christmas decorations.

The war ended, I left home for university, married and went to live in London. My home town had been the victim not only of bombing but also of the depredations of post-war planners. However, to my surprise, on a visit some twenty years later, I managed to locate the tailor's little shop. He was no longer there and his widow explained that she had been running the business since his death; now, however, the little row of old shops was finally about to be demolished and 'redeveloped.' Serendipitously I had called in on her last day in the building!

I told Mrs Marks that I had brought my family on a nostalgic tour of the town and reminded her of the gift of clothes and the Christmas Carousel.

At last I learned their history. Mrs Marks' sister and family had been lucky enough to escape from Germany just before the start of the war. The Carousel, a present from a neighbour in their home town, had been one of the few possessions they had managed to bring with them. One evening, while returning from a visit to friends, the air raid siren had sounded and they had taken refuge in a public shelter. The shelter had received a direct hit. The whole family, including a girl of exactly my age had been killed. The clothes had recently been made by Mr Marks as a present for his young niece and he had not had the heart to dispose of them but had felt pleased that I was going to get some pleasure from them..

Now, after all those years I was shown a faded photograph and also learned the name of the girl whose clothes and Carousel I had inherited. Each Christmas as we light the candles on the Carousel, I remember Leila that pretty ten-year-old girl who will never grow old.

Adjudication

There was a very high standard of entries this year, making it very difficult to choose the winning manuscript.
The Christmas Carol by Anne Everest held my attention and kept me in suspense until the end. It was one I just had to read; a complete story with a beginning, a middle and a very memorable ending. It was entertaining and informative, set against the background of a social commentary of the times.

Chris J. Perry

The Shorter Short Story Competition

Sponsor:

Writers' News

The Writing Magazine

Adjudicator: Mr Ralph Bell

WINNERS & HIGHLY COMMENDED

Competitors were invited to enter compact, illuminating or entertaining short stories up to a strict maximum of 1499 words.

Winners

	Prize	Title	Author / *Pseudonym*
1st	**£100**	**Encounter**	**Wendy Grant** *Gammarus*
2nd	**£60 and dictionary**	**The Dance**	**Pauline Morgan** *Daubenton*
3rd	**£50**	**Poisonous**	**Patricia Thompson** *Bombazine Custard*

Highly Commended

Title	Author	Pseudonym
Night Market	**Jackie Luben**	*Adrianna*
Sniping Crazy	**Nikki Jewell**	*Louise Allison*
Saved	**Mark Fowler**	*Daisychain*
The Room at the Back	**Jan Lee**	*Emanoel*
Birds, Bees and Centipedes	**Peter Rolls**	*Epsilon*
Open and Shut	**Peter Rolls**	*Epsilon*
True to Form	**Stella Marshall**	*C. Fraser*
To Catch a Sprat	**George Scholfield**	*Golly Gee*
Saving Sixpence	**Sion Scott-Wilson**	*Gronow*
Ducks and Drakes	**Mary Churchill**	*Chris Parker*
God Bless	**Karen Meredith**	*Honey Potts*
Would You Adam and Eve It?	**Suzanne Gillespie**	*Louise S Taylor*
Mr McKenzie in Dreamtime	**Mortimer Ribbon**	*Frank Whiteley*
Rubbish	**Richard Salsbury**	*Simon Wren*

ENCOUNTER

WENDY GRANT

The sand had finally settled, though tiny particles still danced and glittered in the air. Ahmid watched the small black shape approaching; it seemed to weave and shimmer, distorted by heat and distance.

His finger tensed against the trigger of his rifle, but the time was not yet. Taking aim too early could be as fatal as waiting too long. He knew his hand could stay perfectly still for only a few seconds – hours of practise had taught him that.

The soldier blinked his reddened eyes, closing them to slits in an unconscious effort to protect himself against the sand which seemed to grind relentlessly into every crease of his skin.

One could see at a glance he was a man of the desert; the camouflaged clothing somehow enhanced the Arab in him. Patiently he waited, wondering what had brought this other man across so many miles of empty land. For himself, getting separated from his unit had just been bad luck. Only Ahmid did not believe in luck, it was, to him, the will of Allah.

Now he saw that his presence here was through design, in order that he could, at this chosen moment in time, annihilate this man – the enemy.

The distant figure began to take shape. Ahmid experienced a flicker of surprise on seeing that the man wore only the simply hooded robe of the desert.

So ... he was no soldier. Ahmid shrugged. It made no difference; he was the enemy and must be destroyed.

His bullets were few and he still had many miles to cross in order to rejoin his unit, to become again part of the army he had vowed to serve. His hand crept along the outer edge of his thigh, brown fingers caressing the knife held fast within the belt.

The man looked quite small, although this may be due to distance creating the illusion. But if Ahmid could use his knife ... so much the better.

Only a few hundred paces now divided them. The figure trudged on, making no effort to deviate from his path.

Ahmid could see no gun, no sign of a weapon, although hand grenades could be hidden beneath the folds of cloth.

His stomach muscles involuntarily contracted, the sensation, almost a pain, dragged a single sound from his cracked lips. 'Aaaah.'

He had only seconds to decide. To waste a bullet when his knife would do the job was foolhardy; to wait and be blown to pieces by a grenade was suicide.

Resolutely he raised the rifle. Sighting the figure he slowly closed one eye.

Nothing happened. The figure continued walking as if blind or stupid. Closer and closer he came, into the small circle pressed against Ahmid's eye.

Ahmid could see the face now in the shadow of the hood. There was no sign of anxiety, no spasm of fear that he had witnessed recently in other men about to die. Only a look of resignation lay there. It seemed to say, 'if I am to die it is the will of Allah.'

But, no man could be so brave, could he? And, if he was the enemy, then he did not have Allah to guide or dictate his future.

When only the length of ten men divided them, Ahmid called out: 'Declare yourself or I shoot.'

The steps faltered. As the dark head tilted back, the hood from the djellaba fell to his shoulders. Dull black eyes stared at Ahmid.

But this was only a boy, no more than eleven or twelve years. He lowered his gun. 'What are you doing here?' he demanded.

The close cropped curls shook from side to side. 'Can you not speak?'

Now words came, tumbling from the boy's parched lips. Ahmid felt a sinking hopeless feeling flood over him. He understood nothing.

'You are the enemy,' he said, trying in vain to make sense of the situation. The boy could have been his son. He should be in school, learning from books that would teach him how to survive one day in his adult world.

But no book had ever given Ahmid a clue how he should behave in war. How to kill a boy of eleven years who was the enemy.

He beckoned to the child. No! He must not think of him as a child – must not allow his emotions to override his logic.

Ahmid marvelled at the boy's courage, for surely he knew that an enemy soldier would kill him.

The boy looked up into Ahmid's face. In his eyes there was no hope, but there was no despair either.

Pulling a flask from his pack, Ahmid unscrewed the top. He reached out, offering precious water to the enemy.

A slow, wondrous smile stretched the swollen lips. The head of tight black curls bowed, then graciously, the boy accepted.

Drinking only a little, aware of the sacrifice Ahmid made, he returned the flask.

Struggling for unfamiliar words he had learned over the passing months of war, Ahmid said, pointing, 'War. You see soldiers?'

Now he understood. Raising his arms the boy mimed shooting, and then dropped to the ground and lay still.

'Dead?' Ahmid asked.

The boy scrambled to his feet and spread his arms. 'All dead?' The soldier's voice was raised in disbelief.

The head nodded, answering the incredulity in the man's voice. 'And your family? Mother? Father?'

Tears squeezed slowly from between swollen eye lids, they made tiny pathways down through the dusty cheeks.

Ahmid sat and stared across the desert. What was he supposed to do? It would be kinder to shoot the boy and end his misery now. With no family, no home, no money, he had no future. There was no one to care what happened to him.

Suddenly, for the first time, Ahmid found himself questioning the rights of war. Against all his training, his belief in dying for the glory of

Allah, doubt crept in through the carefully barred place where his values and beliefs were stored.

A surge of anger rose within him. Someone ought to care – to do something!

His hand dropped to the boy's shoulder. 'I don't know what to do about you. If I leave you here you will die anyhow.'

They sat together, staring out across the barren land.

A snake, appearing as if from nowhere, folded its way across the sand. They watched with detached feelings, until ... suddenly ... it flicked its body, changing direction, striking out at the boy.

Ahmid fired the gun. There had been no time for him to deliberate; the act came from some deep primeval need to survive.

The beautiful patterned body seemed to throw itself into the air, suspended for one moment in space as if basking in the late sunshine. Then it fell slowly in a heap of curved colours before them.

As the body hit the ground the boy rose to his feet. Cautiously he approached, knelt beside the creature, and lifted its head. With his free hand he gestured to Ahmid to pass him the knife.

For one moment the soldier hesitated, and then, with a shrug, he handed it over.

With deft fingers the boy skinned the body. Raising his arm in an arc he threw the head far away from them.

Ahmid watched the young hands scoop a place in the sand in preparation for a fire. Together they gathered some of the dried weed which rolled across the desert.

Soon, the snake, cut into thin strips, was cooking above the flames. They smiled at each other.

At least I will have given him food before I kill him. Ahmid nodded, his obligation of hospitality accomplished so unexpectedly.

White teeth dug into the flesh; it tasted surprisingly good.

Finally they licked their fingers then buried the evidence. Part of Ahmid's mind saw it as a useless task, yet still he did it.

The air was beginning to cool. The time had come to move on. Travelling overnight he would lose less body fluid. He had sufficient water to support him until he reached camp if he was careful.

The dilemma would not go away. Always decisions had been made for him, his function only to carry out orders passed down or barked directly at him by some senior officer. He rose, adjusting his pack, shouldering his gun.

The boy jumped up and stood beside him, waiting, expectant. His eyes, full of trust, observed the man.

Ahmid could feel his heart pounding. Sweat cooled on his skin. Knots tied his stomach. His head seemed about to burst.

Suddenly, in a pure moment of insight, he realised that he had never really had a choice. There was only one thing to do.

Slowly his lips formed into a smile.

Tentatively, the boy smiled back.

Ahmid's arm rested on the boy's shoulders. 'Come,' he said. 'For us the war is done. Let us go home.'

ADJUDICATION

What makes a good story? First, it obviously needs to be a piece of storytelling that will engage its audience. Then, to do that, it needs to be a piece of characterization, written with sufficient skill to make us all identify with the characters. And it needs to capture the character in a moment of time and involved in emotions that say something to us.

That is a fair description of the Shorter Short Story winner, Encounter. *It starts with a good opening. Who is Ahmid? What is he doing there in the desert? That second question is soon answered for us: he is a soldier readying himself to kill an enemy.*

What happens next? That is the question every story should get us asking and Encounter *certainly achieved that. As each twist and surprise is revealed to us, we keep wanting to know what happens next. As the enemy is revealed to us as only a boy, as Ahmid grapples with the dilemma of whether to kill or not, as the snake decides the issue for him and finally as he abandons his soldiering, we are surprised and intrigued. It engages our interest, which is why it is good story telling. Perhaps the strength of the characterization of Ahmid evolves as a character as we read. He develops from a killer-soldier to become a warm, caring human. And the boy acts as a catalyst in this process which we follow with fascination, always wondering what will happen next.*

It is all tightly written and excellently paced-a deserving winner. Congratulations!

Richard Bell

Slim Volume, Small Edition Competition

Sponsor:

rpm print & design

Adjudicator: Jonathan Harry

WINNERS & HIGHLY COMMENDED

Competitors were invited to send a one page (maximum) synopsis, noting the approximate number of words, plus three pages of text only, which were either random or consecutive and a note of any pictures and rough cover ideas, that would enhance the chance to bring the author's dream to book.

Winners

	Prize	Title	Author / *Pseudonym*
1st	**60 books printed & bound (£300)**	**Shoot**	**Jackie Marchant** *Flying Purple Socks*
2nd	**Book prize**	**Six Spoons of Sugar**	**Richard Holdsworth** *St Leonards*
3rd	**Book prize**	**Small Chance**	**W O B Chedzoy** *Derek Gibson*

Highly Commended

Title	Author	Pseudonym
Food Assembly Instructions	**Martin James**	*Roth Jackson*
The Left Handed Child in Primary School	**Brian Hicks**	*Garth Freeman*

SHOOT

JACKIE MARCHANT

Synopsis

Shoot!!! is a basic guide to photography, aimed at those with little or no knowledge of the subject. It would appeal to people who take their cameras out, eager to reproduce special moments, but often find that their snaps don't turn into the images they would have liked. The format would be a slim volume, with 2500 words plus illustrations, which could be stuffed into a suitcase or travel bag and carried around as a guide to use when on holiday or attending a wedding, for example.

Using simple, friendly language, I will explain how a camera works, the merits of different types of camera, how to choose the correct film and how to compose images worthy of preservation in the family album. Shoot!!! will be illustrated with my own images.

I will briefly mention the importance of aperture and shutter speed and how these can be manipulated to produce 'arty' photography. Although most cameras are fully automatic and there is no need to worry about manual settings, this background information is useful when composing shots.

I will outline in some detail the important rules of composition, which can influence the way holiday snaps turn out. I will give tips on how to second guess the setting an automatic camera will choose and the best way to use this to your advantage. There will be a section on common faults and how to avoid them, plus general advice. I will give pointers on how to show everyone your photos without boring them senseless.

Finally, my bibliography will suggest books for those who want to take the subject further.

Choosing Your Camera

Imagine a box, which is black inside and sealed from the light. Stretched across the back of the box is a light sensitive film. At the front of the box, opposite the film, a small hole allows light to hit the film for a short period of time. The light reacts with the film, producing a latent image: that is, if you could see into the black box at this time, you wouldn't see anything on the film. But once the film has been developed and printed, then you have your photo.

Put a lens and a shutter, which can be controlled by pressing a button, over the hole and you have a camera.

By controlling the size of the hole and length of time light is allowed in, you control the way your final image will look. There are many good automatic cameras on the market, so all you have to do is point and shoot and let the camera choose its own settings. But it is with manual control that a photographer can produce an artistic image and it is worth understanding how to achieve this, whether you are happy to simply point and shoot or not.

There are four basic types of camera - disposable, compact, single lens reflex (SLR) and digital.

Disposable Camera

This is the simplest type of camera, which comes with a film inside. There are no controls other than the shutter (the button you press to take your photo) and once the film has been shot, the whole camera goes to the lab where it is broken open and the film processed. This type of camera can only be used for one film. They are ideal for beginners and for use on holiday, if you've forgotten your camera or need a waterproof one for the beach. They take reasonable pictures, but constant use of disposables can be expensive. Always use a good brand of disposable camera.

Compact Camera

This is the point and shoot variety and perfectly adequate for taking good quality snaps. These are fully automatic cameras and may have a zoom lens. They are inexpensive, simple to use and take a good quality photograph. They are ideal for quick pictures, such as holiday snaps and with a bit of knowledge about composition, you can take stunning shots with them. For complete artistic freedom though, you will need an SLR.

Single Lens Reflex Camera

Generally known as an SLR. A mirror inside the camera allows the photographer to use the viewfinder to see exactly what the lens is seeing. These cameras may be manual or automatic and are normally both with an auto focus option. They can be used with a variety of lenses and flash equipment. They are more difficult to use, can be very expensive and are bulkier than a compact camera, but an SLR is essential for those moody, arty shots. This is the sort of camera that the professional uses, and may be worth a try if you want to have a go at being arty with your camera. Some camera shops sell second-hand SLRs.

Digital Camera

A relatively new innovation, the digital camera does not use film. Instead, the image is recorded onto a disc, which can be read by a computer. Images can be emailed, displayed on a computer or television screen, printed onto photo-paper at home, or developed from disc in a lab. Shots can be viewed immediately and kept or discarded.

Digital cameras are more costly than the point and shoot and, as yet, the quality of the digital photograph is inferior to that of the conventional film photo. But technology is constantly improving and some digital cameras are producing images good enough for the professional. However, these cameras are extremely expensive.

Choosing The Right Film

Many people believe that a cheap camera won't take as good a picture as an expensive one. This is not necessarily true. Very expensive cameras will have specialist lenses, but compact cameras can take high quality images as long as the correct film is used.

First of all, always use good quality film. Avoid the free films offered as part of a processing package and avoid supermarket or store chain brands. It is best to stick to well-known, reliable brands such as Kodak, Fuji or Agfa. Before buying film, always check the use by date and never buy film that is near to, or past, its use by date.

Next, look for the ISO (formerly ASA) number, which will be stamped on the box of film. Most people know that this relates to the speed of film, but what does that mean? The lower the number of the rating, the slower the film will react with light. This is very important. If you are going on holiday to a sunny clime, then you should use a film with a slow speed, for example: 100 or 200. If you use a faster speed for example: 400, you will find your shots will all be over exposed and look wishy-washy, or your automatic camera will refuse to take that lovely shot you'd like to show everyone when you get home.

On the other hand, if you are taking your camera out on a dull day in England, you should be using a faster film: 400 is ideal. The film will react more quickly to light, enabling you to take shots in dull conditions.

Very fast film (1600) can be used in poor light conditions and is ideal for capturing those moody sunsets. But the image can appear grainy if there is insufficient light.

ADJUDICATION

Shoot was chosen as the First Prize winner because it is a clear and concisely written idea for a book with a very well defined and large market.
It covers the basics of photography aimed at those with little or no knowledge of the subject. Such mysteries as choosing the right film are covered. All useful stuff!
The concept of the book is inviting the reader to achieve better snapshots and it's not overtly technical.
Congratulations!

Jonathan Harry

Haiku Competition

Sponsor:

The British Haiku Society

Adjudicator: Stanley Pelter

WINNERS & HIGHLY COMMENDED

Competitors of all ages were invited to submit Haibun which could be as short as desired but no longer than 1000 words, including haiku that could be structured in the classical three lines, 5-7-5 syllable form or in the more contemporary western 'free-form' style. The haiku could not be more than 17 syllables and the inclusion of a seasonal word was optional. The haibun is not a genre that allows for dedicated hints of what might follow any more than couplets do. Only complete pieces of work were considered.

Winners

	Prize	Title	Author / *Pseudonym*
1st	**Book prize & S. Pelter Trophy**	**Walking on the Margins**	**Judith Allnatt** *Sargasso*
2nd	**Book prize**	**A Journey with my Father**	**Anne Brooke** *Dreamer*

Highly Commended

Title	Author	Pseudonym
After Spring Rain	**Alex Swinburn**	*Alex Romanovsky*
An Alphanumerical Journey	**Joanna Ray**	*Rufaro*
Tall Grass	**Stephanie Cherril**	*Shauna Mercury*

Note: A third prize was not awarded.

HAIBUN

JUDITH ALLNATT

Walking on the Margins

After days of rain the sun uncurls leaves and opens doors. The country park is full of the treble sounds of children and birds, crying out for attention from the arcing swings and the top of the slide, from the shadowed nests and the tips of birch branches. Young call to their mothers in a green springing world.

My children are older, they play football on the open field and call out to each other. When I join in, I am fumble-footed, too cautious , too slow. I provide the goal posts. Leaving my cardigan and the picnic bag on the grass, generously spaced, I withdraw.

wasps and cyclists zing
around the park-wings and spokes
a heat haze

I take the tunnelled shade for the path down to the lake. Keen types with backpacks overtake me, then a jogger checking his time as he runs. Only the mum with a buggy full of sleeping baby is stoller-slow. The baby is hot-cheeked and sticky under a nodding parasol. I give the mum a smile for him and she accepts it, tucks it away along with the feathers and picked flowers of the day.

I reach the brightness of the lake, flood water shining back at the sky and stop where it laps at my feet. The picnic tables are still under water after the rains.

The water, almost still, spreads light up into the branches of the half-drowned trees. Their trunks are like pillars, reflected, turned to marble by spangling light.

geese with evening-glove necks
beckon on the glass lake
for the last dance

Adjudication

Thank you for submitting and allowing me to read and comment on your haibun.
First, may I congratulate you on being awarded first place in this competition.
The haibun might be more effective if a haiku, to textualise the prose, occurred as the starting point, even though I like the evocation of personal experience that rings true throughout the piece. I also enjoyed the fact that the haiku add rather than repeat what is being said in the prose and the high quality of literary devices employed combined with the delicate understatements contained within them.

The haiku are of a more variable quality. Although the imagery of the 'geese' poem appeals, the continuous sentence format and the over-emphatic mingling of the geese with the human activity of 'beckoning for the last dance' does jar. From these points of view the first haiku is more effective. One other detail in terms of language is the phrase 'keen types with backpacks'. But the negatives are magnificently out-weighed by the large number of positives. The lesson, I suppose, is that due to the brevity and special characteristics of haibun, it is even more important in this genre that the unity of the work is watertight, with every word and phrase, intonation and implication considered and re-considered before final commitment. Nothing extraneous should be in the final document.
Again, congratulations.

Stanley Pelter

Local History Competition

Sponsor:

Hampshire County Council

Adjudicator: Michael Hicks

WINNERS & HIGHLY COMMENDED

Competitors were invited to submit well-documented and referenced manuscripts describing any aspect of local history in Hampshire. They could include photographs, sketches, maps and other illustrations. Minimum of 1000 words, maximum 10,000 words.

Winners

	Prize	Title	Author / *Pseudonym*
1st	**£100 & The Margaret Kryle trophy**	**Layton's of Andover**	**David J. Borrett** *Ross Kingsley*
2nd	**£75**	**W M Bache, An Eighteenth Century Ordinance Officer**	**Lesley Burton** *Tony Laver*
3rd	**£50**	**A Brief History of Rowlands Castle**	**J. Dicks** *Littleton*

Highly Commended

Title	Author	Pseudonym
James Norton, 'East Worldham'	**Rupert Willoughby**	*Baker*

LAYTON'S OF ANDOVER

DAVID J. BORRETT

The History of a China and Glass Warehouse 1853-1952

The old line of shops that once stood behind the Guildhall was demolished in the late 1960s to make way for Town Development. One of the most attractive of these buildings was on the eastern corner, popularly remembered as Scott's shoe shop, but before that, the offices of Poore's Brewery. The decorative brickwork façade of the structure is visible in many photographs of the High Street, as are the buildings at the other end of the row. However, the several shops that lay directly behind the Guildhall rarely attracted the photographer's eye, until in 1967 Charles Wardell undertook the task of producing a series of shots of the old part of the town, including several views of this particular line of buildings. It was a last look round just before the bulldozers moved in.[1]

Immediately next to Scott's was a classically Georgian building of quiet market town style, rather similar to some of those still surviving in East Street. By 1967, it had been the greengrocery of Reg. Elwick for about fifteen years, and before that, for a very short time, the premises of a relative of his, a Mr Booth, whose own greengrocery tenure ended abruptly after his criminal involvement with stolen motor vehicles became the subject of legal proceedings. The episode was in stark contrast to the continuity of previous years, as prior to that, No 49 High Street had long been home to the china and glass emporium known as Rosa E. Layton, a family enterprise that had been established in 1853.

The building's outer façade was predominantly of early nineteenth century origin, having a tiled roof with three evenly-spaced dormer windows above a dentil frieze. Five sliding sash windows lined the red-bricked upper floor while at ground floor level (in 1967) there were three shop windows, separated by two single doorways, each with two stone steps. The shop window at the western end of the building was a late addition and replaced two sash windows, similar to those in the storey above. Until then, this part of the building, together with the adjacent door, was part of the living accommodation. These alterations were carried out some time during the first half of the twentieth century – certainly after 1907.[2]

Zaccheus Layton, who first established the china and glass business there, was a native of Aylesbury, born in 1816. The name Layton was a local one to that area, and early spellings can be traced as Laighton, Leyghton and Layghton in sixteenth and seventeenth century parish records, becoming standardised as Layton by the eighteenth century. In 1811 Zaccheus Layton's parents were married in the parish church of St Mary's Aylesbury. Evidently they were nonconformists as each successive child – all boys – were baptised at Hale Leys Independent Chapel (the law did not then allow marriage in unlicensed buildings such as nonconformist chapels and dissenters had to marry in the parish church). But misfortune seemed to strike the Layton parents over the name John. The first, baptised in 1820, died as an infant, and then a second given the same name, baptised in 1824, suffered the same fate. This double tragedy might have been the reason why the Laytons had a change of religious heart, for they subsequently withdrew their allegiance to the Independent Chapel and returned to Anglicanism. This was publicly demonstrated by all the surviving children being baptised for a second time at the parish church of St. Mary's, Aylesbury on 23rd August 1829.

By the mid 1840s, Zaccheus had married Hannah and was living in Newbury. Three children were born there, William, Robert and Louisa (Lucy), before the family moved to Andover in about 1852-3 when Walter was born. The 1861 census for Andover lists two further children, Frank aged seven and Arthur aged three, although Walter is then absent from the family home. Zaccheus is described as an *earthenware* dealer. This suggests a more utilitarian type of stock-in-trade at this point, although it may have just been the census enumerator's blanket term. Whites Directory of 1859 and the Post Office directory for 1867 list Zaccheus as a china and glass dealer, as do later directories, but here too, we cannot be sure that the term was not an "in-house" one, applied to all such trades. When first setting up business we might expect Zaccheus to begin with domestic ware which would not have cost so much to stock, and then develop into more expensive lines if trade proved successful. But at the same time he would have continued to sell the cheaper goods as well; in a small town the kitchen was just as important, if not more so, than the drawing room, and an astute businessman would not have forgotten that there was money to be made from pots as well as porcelain. Indeed, years later, when the business was well-established, the shop continued to supply wares of diverse quality and level because there was a healthy demand for all.

As the children grew up they seem to have scattered. Robert moved to Whitechapel, London, married Eliza and had three children, but by 1873 the family was back in Andover, with Robert running what was then commonly known as a marine store, at 87 High Street. He was more precisely described as a "wholesale and retail rag, bone and metal merchant, and a coal merchant" in a directory of 1880, but by 1889 was a greengrocer, a trade in which he stayed engaged until the shop was taken over by Alfred Gorey about the beginning of the First World War. The six children attended Miss Gale's Infant School.[3]

Another of Zaccheus' children who left and then returned to the town was Walter, who would eventually succeed his father as proprietor of the china and glass business at No 49 High Street. Apprenticed as a cabinet maker, the 1871 census lists him as 18 years old and living with the family above the shop. The other family occupants were Louisa, then 19, Frank, an apprentice carpenter, and 13 year-old Arthur. Zaccheus was now aged 54 and Hannah, his wife, 46. Ten years later, in 1881, Hannah was dead and all the children had left home. Only Zaccheus remained, with a housekeeper, a domestic servant and a lodger installed.

Families may disperse in all directions but Walter had gone farther than most. He does not appear on the 1881 census because he was almost certainly in the United States where he was married, and then widowed. The brief union produced one daughter, Jenny. In 1889, Zaccheus died, and by then Walter had returned to Andover, as he took over the running of the shop. His daughter who lived with him was then aged five.

On 7th April 1890, in a civil ceremony, Walter married Rosa Elizabeth Banks, a 27 year-old governess whose late mother had derived her income from the possession of several local properties, the revenue from which was shared between Rosa and her brother William. Her father who had died years before was James Banks, a coal merchant of Bridge Street. Rosa was not poor and she was possessed of a good business brain. Although the 36 year-old Walter was almost ten years her senior, it may have seemed a good match. It is difficult to know exactly when Walter returned to the town and whether he was running the shop prior to his father's death. Possibly Rosa had been Jenny's governess; her home address was just across the street from Walter's, near the entrance to Union Street; being so close to Walter's shop, she would have made the ideal choice if a governess had been sought to look after Jenny.

The marriage produced two children – Leslie Banks in 1891 and Gladys Charlotte in 1892 who both attended Gale's School for a short time before being sent to a private school in 1899. The shop which Walter ran, and Rosa helped to finance, was apparently successful. A commercial review of the business written about 1891 pays tribute to Walter's "vigour and enterprise…securing every advantage in the matter of price that can result from large orders, judiciously placed." In describing the type of stock we learn from the report that "the leading manufacturers…are represented, including Minton, Worcester, Staffordshire, Derby, Wedgwood and Copeland. Every taste and every requirement…has been fully catered for, and a copiousness of selection is offered that leaves nothing to be desired. The leading lines…are dinner, tea and dessert services, in every style and at all prices, toilet and chamber sets, plates, dishes, jugs, artistic-cut table glass, decanters, flower-stands, bowls, English, French, and Dresden fancy goods, and a full line of general and useful earthenware" which included a large variety of Doulton's art pottery. We also learn that "all kinds of goods are lent on hire for school treats, private parties, and public banquets" and the shop is patronised by "the leading families, hotel proprietors, and licensed victuallers, and the smaller shopkeepers of the district." As a final tribute, the correspondent writes of "Mr Layton" being "an able, intelligent, and pushing tradesman, fair and honourable in all his dealings, and commanding the confidence of all who come into business relations with him."[4]

Walter's qualities as a shopkeeper and general purveyor of goodwill undoubtedly impressed the reviewer, but life above the shop did not present quite the same picture; wherever and however the difficulties surfaced, Rosa and Walter's marriage soon began to crumble, and by 1895, plans were being drawn up to effect a legal separation. The subsequent Minutes of Arrangement gave Rosa custody of the children and the tenancy of the shop. In return she agreed to pay Walter his share of the assets of the business, after making allowance for the book debts (those who owed the business for goods taken on account). It appears that Walter had already borrowed the sum of £274/18/4d from Rosa, so this was also deducted from the final amount paid over.[5] An indenture made on the 8th January 1896 states that a valuation of the assets carried out by Allan Herbert was calculated at £1,376/9/8d, from which was deducted the loan and the book debts, leaving £716/13/10d to be divided between them.[6] From this moment on, both Walter and his daughter Jenny seem to vanish.[7] Possibly they returned to America.

Under Rosa's stewardship, the shop flourished as she adapted her trade to cater for the changing circumstances of the age. By the turn of the century, travelling had become a national pursuit, and a profitable development for china dealers up and down the country was the sale of novelties printed with the borough crest or a local scene, for sale to day trippers and tourists. These were specially commissioned from the Staffordshire factories in a variety of standard shapes ranging from miniature vases and animals through to models of transport and household gadgets. Attractively priced, crested and pictorial china ornaments were not only bought by visitors, but also by the town's inhabitants. Soon Rosa was styling herself as "Agent for Foley Andover Arms China". Foley was the trade name of one of the more prolific factories producing such wares, and an added advantage in selling this was that Rosa could advertise the business; each was marked underneath with the legend "Rosa E. Layton, 49 High St, Andover".

An advertisement of 1907 incorporates a rare view of Layton's business premises.[8] This was prior to the alteration which provided another shop window to the left, but the length of the overhead sign-writing shows clearly that the unaltered section was nonetheless part of the same premises. Outside are displayed stoneware crocks and jars, and farther along, some large meat dishes of ordinary Staffordshire quality. In the windows, there seems to be a vast array of jugs, many in graduated sets which were also standard household ware. Just discernible is a variety of stoneware hunting jugs which were issued by Royal Doulton in two tones of brown and applied with various sporting motifs, popular at this period. The open door fails to reveal any detail of exactly what was inside but it is evident that the shop was well-stocked with goods laid out from floor level upwards. Possibly Rosa departed a little from the path that her husband had tried to follow when he stocked the wares of the "leading manufacturers". From Rosa's point of view, although it may have been prestigious to display the finest Minton, Worcester, Derby and Spode, and undoubtedly there were many families in the area with sufficient wealth to purchase it, perhaps the shop's accounts suggested that the balance was out of kilter for an ordinary market town like Andover. There was a profusion of other factories in the Potteries who, though less eminent, could supply excellent china at a cheaper price, and a good mixture of qualities and price may well have been a more viable commercial proposition. However, perhaps it would be wrong to overplay any differences in trading style between Walter and Rosa; the fulsome language of the 1891 review suggests that the writer would likely exaggerate the more up-market side of the business while choosing to pass over its less impressive, workaday elements. And customer demand in 1907 may not have been quite the same as that of 1891. Consumer fashions were as potent then as they are today.

The 1907 advertisement shows that the business was, in the language of the day, a "china and glass warehouse", both wholesale and retail. Rosa claimed that she was a contractor for His Majesty's Government (probably she supplied the expanding military presence in the area) and, as in Walter's day, goods, including cutlery and silver, could be lent on hire. In addition, glass and china repairs were undertaken, probably effected by the use of metal rivets, and often said to have been the work of the travelling gypsies. No doubt Rosa had regular callers and contacts, travellers or not, who would do such work. Evidently, there was more to the business than simple retailing and Rosa's formula must have been an effective one for her pre-eminence in Andover was long held, and during her time no other similar establishment set up in direct competition. Admittedly, Parsons and Hart whose trade was house furnishing, might include china and glass in one of their departments; and the family business of Holmes, the publishers of the *Andover Advertiser,* sold ceramic ware as part of their stock of fancy goods, but it would be wrong to think either of these were china and glass dealers per se. Only Rosa E. Layton could lay claim to that.

Unfortunately, it is only near the end of Rosa's time that we can be on firmer ground in pinpointing more precisely some of the aspects of her business practice. Three day books, charting the period from 1931 to 1943, survive among the records at Winchester Record Office, deposited by the Clerk of the Works in 1970, after the premises had been consigned to rubble - probably a last-minute find by the contractors when preparing to build the new town centre.[9] The period covered by these books mark a time both of national and personal upheaval. Possibly by the early 1930s Rosa had passed on the running of the shop to her son Leslie Banks Layton; her later years were beset by "prolonged illness", and after her death on 13th February 1936, aged 75, the business was continued by Leslie, without any noticeable interruption. During the period Rosa had been proprietor, from 1896 onwards, the population of Andover had been steadily increasing, rising from just over 6000 people to reach over 10,000 by the 1930s. The favourable expansion of both people and houses was obviously a contributing factor to the shop's success and at some point Rosa had also purchased the freehold of the building.

From the names of the firms with which the shop dealt in the 1930s, it is easier to assess the type of stock. Certainly there was still much that was utilitarian: T. G. Green, Grindley and Co. and Bovey Tracey Pottery produced kitchenalia and dinnerware of ordinary quality while more decorative objects, albeit mass-produced for the lower end of the market, were turned out by factories such as Hancock and Sons and Burgess Bros. Typical were sets of graduated jugs, pairs of vases and dessert wares of printed designs on an earthenware body that was overlaid with cheap gilding. Another factory with which Rosa did business was the works at Aller Vale who made terra-cotta country pottery of red Devon clay painted with such motifs as cockerels, mottoes and cottages. Dealings were also with firms such as Plant and Co, Shelley and Aynsley which were then considered secondary manufacturers of finer quality products. Familiar names such as Wedgwood, Copeland and Royal Doulton also appear in Rosa's accounts; by the 1930s, each of these firms had reached a zenith of output that encompassed a vast range including earthenware services of standard printed patterns, artist-designed hand-crafted stoneware and top quality, individually-painted and signed cabinet porcelain of rich ground colours and raised gilding. Rosa might have chosen to stock any of this; the obvious diversity of her enterprise would no doubt have tempted her to include at least a smattering of what was both sumptuous and expensive. Aside from china and glass, Layton's seem to have sold brooms and mops too as there are regular sales of these on account during the 1930s. Perhaps they had a good source of supply and were able to undercut everyone else.

Manufacturers and suppliers of glassware are also recorded: J. Wuidart were Belgian importers with warehouses at Bartlett's Buildings in London from whom Rosa could have ordered a range of products without having to deal with individual firms. Both British and foreign products could be bought from them at competitive prices, and the innovative glass made by James Powell and Sons, marketed as Whitefriars, was a staple line during the 1930s. The firm of Jobling and Co was a manufacturer with which Rosa dealt directly. A popular product for them during this period was opalescent and blue tinted moulded glass in imitation of Lalique. Cut glass was supplied by either Edinburgh and Reith or Thomas Webb while some of the pressed glass came from the factory of Davidson and Co of Gateshead. Everything arrived at the shop in crates which were sent back by rail. Cheques were periodically written out to individual firms in settlement of accounts. Sometimes, items were not delivered or they arrived broken in which case adjustments had to be made.

Many of Rosa's customers, especially if they were either fellow traders or regular purchasers, kept running accounts. In those days, before the advent of chain stores and nationally-based concerns, high street business was provided by independent, local people operating in a relatively small way. In order that each could thrive, the collective interest was best served by local money being kept within the confines of the local circle, and so each dutifully patronised the other. It was not just a question of convenience and loyalty, but a sound principle for survival. So we see that a bicycle was purchased from F. Harvey of No 78 High Street for £8/12/6d, presumably for deliveries, and whenever, Mr Harvey required replacements for china that was broken or perhaps needed to purchase a suitable wedding present, he went to Layton's. It may be coincidence but when in December 1942 Leslie sent a cheque for £1/1/- to the Mayor's Christmas Fund, five days later the Mayoress, Mrs Bell, came in and bought a set of toilet ware for 15/11d. In the mid 1930s Dr Hodgson purchased a tea service for 11/6d, as did Mr Crang a lesser one. The latter, a local ironmonger, received a discount of 10d on his 8/6d. T. Lynn and Sons were frequent customers, and as an example of how in those days people could obtain replacements without spending more than was strictly necessary, we see that Mrs Buckland, wife of the proprietor of the large draper's shop just around the corner in Upper High Street, was supplied with a vegetable dish made to fit her existing cover for 5/11d.

Account transactions were often of menial value. Just because people were relatively wealthy did not mean they regularly spent large sums: on 23rd February 1932, the Countess of Portsmouth bought 1 "Yuan" (a standard blue and white pattern made by Woods) saucer for 5d and 2 tea plates for 10d, while on the 26th August, Mrs T. Webb (wife of one of the Freemen of the Borough) bought three 2lb jampots at 6½d each. The Hon. Bryan Guinness of Biddesden House, whose short-lived marriage to the former Diana Mitford ended in 1933 when she left him for Sir Oswald Mosley, was also a client whose name regularly appears in the records for diverse orders of small value. All such purchases were recorded for settlement at a later date. Of course there were also cash sales, but these did not require any special treatment except the total amount being entered for each day.

The 1930s was a difficult period for retailing. Sales on account for the financial year that ended 31st March 1932 were £636/13/5d. Without records for previous years it is impossible to gauge how good or bad this was. Certainly it was much better than the following year when account sales dipped to £464/10/2d. 1933-34 was little better at £486/10/2d. From then on things improved slowly and by March 1937, the sales on account that year had reached £619/13/-. Cash sales varied tremendously from day to day. Fridays were often the best while Wednesdays, which would have been mornings only, were quiet. Anything between £1 and £10 seems to have been a normal daily take, with £3 to £6 being a reasonable average. Perhaps the figures between 1932 and 1936 owe something to Rosa's withdrawal from the business through illness, and are not wholly attributable to the effects of the economic slump.

After Rosa's death, the business was continued by her son Leslie who styled himself L. Banks Layton, although the shop kept its business name of Rosa E. Layton. He was still a bachelor and quite possibly, he had been employed by his mother all his working life. Indeed, it may well be the sixteen-year-old Leslie who is standing on the doorstep in the 1907 advertisement. The older gentleman in the picture, though looking very much like a proprietor, is probably Rosa's manager.[10] It is unlikely to be Walter, as by this time Rosa and he had long since separated.

The middle of the 1930s was marked by Royal celebrations – the Silver Jubilee of King George V and Queen Mary, the proposed Coronation of King Edward VIII and the actual Coronation of King George VI and Queen Elizabeth. With each successive event, china dealers could rely on the sale of commemorative wares produced for the occasion. The abdication of Edward VIII, although five months before the planned coronation date, did not prevent the sale of a vast quantity of mugs, plates, cups and saucers and other sundry articles to private purchasers, all manufactured and in the shops well in advance. For both factories and dealers, the constitutional upset was by no means a total loss as most people probably bought similar wares again for the Coronation of King George VI, scheduled for the same date – 12th May 1937. In Andover, as elsewhere, the Borough Council issued mugs to all the children of the town, both in 1935 and 1937, inscribed with Andover and the name of the Mayor, B. Shaw Porter, who was in office on both occasions. The cost of each local celebration, including the purchase of mugs for the children, was raised through the Council levying an extra 1d on the rates. Disappointingly for Rosa E. Layton however, though the business should have been ideally placed to supply the mugs, there is no record in the day books of any transaction to this effect, so it seems the Council must have dealt directly with the manufacturer.[11] Of course the Council had to be sure to secure the commemorative mugs at an economical price as they were spending ratepayers' money.

Despite passing over Layton's to supply the mugs, the Mayor, B. Shaw-Porter, was a regular customer; whenever, he proposed to hold a large dinner or tea, he hired the requisite china. For example on 24th December 1936, 230 tea-cups, saucers and tea-plates, and 100 medium plates, together with three large jugs were ordered at a total hire cost of 15/11d. A fortnight later, more crockery was hired for a smaller occasion. Cutlery was also available and Mrs Portsmouth ordered 154 large forks and 139 dessert spoons, together with 36 large jugs the week following the coronation at a cost of 16/9d. Breakages and shortfalls were charged after their return - 5d for a tea-plate and 2/- for a jug.

The business must have sold a great deal of commemorative china during the celebrations, and there were evidently several varieties on sale in the shop. Just before Jubilee day in 1935, Mrs Yorke Scarlett bought 31 mugs and 28 cups, saucers and plates, spending a total of £2/13/4d, while Mrs Elmes bought 36 mugs at 10/6d a dozen. An advertisement which ran for many weeks on the front page of the local newspaper in 1937 informed the reader that a range of "Coronation china" was now available at Layton's. A week before the event, Mrs T. Clark bought two mugs at 9d each while Mrs Elmes this time bought just six at 6d and Mrs Hartigan bought another six at 3d each. Hartigan's was a well-known racing stables, so perhaps the mugs were for the jockeys or the stable lads. These were all relatively inexpensive versions, but there were better examples on offer. Mrs McCleod bought a mug for 1/9d and a tobacco jar for 3/6d. The bone china cup and saucer illustrated, manufactured by Plant and Co of Longton, would have cost several shillings. Certainly it was purchased at Layton's because it bears a paper label to that effect underneath.

Notes at the beginning of the daybooks detail some of the annual insurances which had to be paid: £2/12/6d was enough to cover £1500 of stock (an indication of the stock level at that time) while 17/6d covered employees. The premium for windows was set at £1/5/- while the value of the premises, then estimated at £4,500, required £4/10/- . Insurances were also paid on dwellings around the town for which Rosa, and later Leslie, received rent. Some of these were likely purchased years before by Rosa'a father and included Nos. 9 and 13 Vigo Road, 17 and 41 West Street, one house in London Street, and another dwelling in Adelaide Road. However, newer houses like 26 and 28 Charlton Road and also 113 Old Winton Road, must have been bought by Rosa herself.[12] It seems if business warranted it, she invested surplus money into buying to let.

There were other regular expenses: an advertisement in the Parish Magazine cost 9/- annually, while 200lbs of 40 x 48 brown paper for wrapping, was purchased at 14/- cwt. An advertisement in Kelly's Andover Directory for two years was £2/10/- while a listing in Kelly's Hampshire Directory was 7/- for four years. And a regular subscription to the Pottery Gazette at 15/- kept Rosa and Leslie in regular touch with innovations and fashions in the industry. In order to further the chance of attracting new customers, in 1933 the shop was advertising in the programmes issued by the New Theatre (later the Rex Cinema) in West Street at 1/- a month. However, in 1938, Leslie was refused an advert in the chapel magazine, and on 4th June 1940, his regular placing in the *Andover Advertiser* was cancelled by him because the charge had increased by 16/3d.[13]

In the early years of war, there seems to have been a difficulty in keeping staff: "Smith", who had joined as a sixteen-year-old in December 1932, left in June 1940 to join up. Leslie then hired fifteen-year-old Bertie Leonard Hallett who left after two weeks, followed by F. H. James Leader who was taken on in the middle of July, and left before the middle of August. On April 21st 1941, Henry Tully, aged seventeen, of 54 South Street, started, but finished within a week! Leslie was more successful with Len Smith who was taken on in May 1941, and stayed eighteen months until November 1942, followed by Harold Ayres Cook who remained until September 1943.[14] Although the war was on, in none of these cases were the boys old enough for statutory conscription; we might conclude that while "Smith" had suited him well enough and may of course have been tutored by Rosa, Leslie could be a tough employer on those not familiar with his way of doing things.

During the war, most factories ceased production altogether and anything produced for the domestic market was devoid of colour or restricted to a few drab-looking tones. Leslie noted in the daybook in April 1942 the "Houses good for supplying in Wartime". These included Doulton & Co, Wild & Sons, Grindley's, Wilkinson, Rankin & Co, Plant, Meakin, Howard Pottery and New Hall Pottery. A useful sale in December 1942 was that of twelve teapots to the R.A.F. Sergeant's Mess at 4/9d each, and at the end of the following January, Mrs Cope from the White Hart Hotel in Bridge street purchased casseroles, glass jugs, a cruet and eight glass spoons for a total of £1/19/8d. Although the war ended in 1945, the severe restrictions on production continued to be imposed for many years and it was not until the early 1950s that colour again began to creep back into home market crockery.

Those who thought Leslie a confirmed old bachelor must have been surprised in 1947 when he married Mrs Doreen Lavinia Riley, a widow with two teenage daughters. Initially, they lived above the shop at 49 High Street, but eventually it was decided to close the shop and move to a house in Junction Road. Leslie was now 60 and he opted for retirement. He retained ownership of the shop which became the greengrocery run by Reg Elwick. This remained so until Town Development forced the closure and demolition of all the shops both behind the Guildhall and in the West Street area. The condemned buildings were all compulsorily purchased in 1964 by Andover Borough Council.[15] Leslie's widow carried out the conveyance as he had died three years earlier on 29th August 1961. However, the plans for Town Development had been officially drawn up before his death and he is said to have been saddened by his old family premises' likely demise.[16]

Closing in 1952, Layton's had been established in Andover for 99 years. Only a few Andover businesses have surpassed that length of tenure.[17] The gap in the market was filled by The China Mart which was located at No 1 London Street and The Pottery Shop in Bridge Street, but by the early 1970s only T. Lynn & Sons, principally ironmongers, and also to a small degree, Holmes and Sons, were dealing in high-class china and glass. The other two specialists had disappeared.

In recent years, demand for more standard ware was filled by Timothy Whites, now defunct, and one or two others who included it as part of a general stock. The privately-run concern known as Chantry China, originally in Union Street and at present near the top of the Upper High Street, is alone in retailing better quality goods - just one shop to serve a population of over 35,000 people. One suspects Rosa, given such a potential clientele, would have been rubbing her hands with glee.

References

1. A set of these photographs are deposited in Andover Reference Library.
2. An illustration of the building before alteration appears in Hampshire and the Isle of Wight by Pen and Camera, published in 1907 by William Mate and Sons Ltd. (Winchester Reference Library, POO1468995, Class SH12, No.10692).
3. HRO 208M86/1-3, Gales School Admission Register.
4. Industrial Great Britain, A Commercial Review of Leading Firms Selected from Important Towns of England, London Printing and Engraving Company n.d. (c.1891).
5. HRO 46M84, Box 70, Minutes of Arrangement, 16th December 1895, between Walter Layton and Rosa Elizabeth Layton.
6. HRO 46M84, Box 70, Indenture, 8th January 1896.
7. Neither appears in the computer-indexed 1901 Census of England and Wales, nor is Walter's death registered before that year. Moreover, at the time of his daughter Gladys Charlotte's marriage in 1913, he is presumably still living as the certificate states, under father of the bride: "Walter Layton, china merchant", without the addition of the usual "(deceased)".
8. Hampshire and Isle of Wight by Pen and Camera, William Mate and Sons, 1907.
9. HRO 90M70/B1-2-3. Day Books, 1931-43.
10. When Rosa came to draw up her will in 1934, she left a bequest to her manager.
11. The 1935 mugs I have seen have no manufacturers stamp, but the 1937 versions are marked Grimwade's Royal Winton.
12. Rosa's brother, William James Banks left some properties to her in his will.
13. HRO 90M70/B1-2-3. Day Books, 1931-43.
14. Ibid.
15. Documents relating to compulsory purchases by Andover Borough Council. Their reference: HP 74185. Beech Hurst Council Offices.
16. Information supplied by Miss June M. Harris.
17. Retail businesses that were long-lived include: Shaw and Sons, Harvey's, Holmes, T. Lynn, Pearse's, and Parsons and Hart.

List of Illustrations

1. Detail from the 1873 Ordnance Survey Map. Scale: 10.56 feet to one statute mile, 41.66 ft to one inch. The Layton building is second from the right behind the Town Hall.
2. 1907 advertisement from Hampshire and Isle of Wight with Pen and Camera, published by W.Mate.
3. Portrait photograph of Leslie Banks Layton c. 1908, taken by Fred Wright, Andover.
4. View of the Upper High Street c. 1908, taken by Francis Frith, showing part of the shop front of Layton's.
5. Bone china cup and saucer made by R. Plant and Co. This bears a Layton label and was sold by them at the time of the coronation of King George VI and Queen Elizabeth.
6. View of the shops behind the Guildhall in 1967, one of a series taken by Charles Wardell recording the old town before development. By this time the premises were those of Reg. Elwick, greengrocer.

Adjudication

This is a well-researched and well-written account of a lost business that is potentially of much more than local interest. There were china and glass shops in all Andover's equivalents everywhere. The lost premises, the family and the history of the business are treated satisfactorily, although there are comments and corrections to be made, but the study is lifted to another plane by the analysis of the surviving account which illuminates daily, weekly and annual sales, stock in trade and customers.

Yet records could have been used to cast more light on the clientele, their numbers, spending patterns, social and geographical distribution and hence the market that Layton's served. With that addition, this could be a paper that is a compulsory port of call for historians of retailing and similar firms everywhere and would be suitable for Hampshire Studies.

Michael Hicks

Young Writers' Poetry Competition

Sponsors:

Hampshire & Isle of Wight Youth Options

Adjudicator: Keith Bennett, Founder, The New Forest Poetry Society

WINNERS & HIGHLY COMMENDED

Competitors were invited to send poems, no more than 30 lines as follows: age group 6-11: wrote about their own freedom and that of their family and friends; age 12-15: wrote about choices, restriction, independence and free will; age 16-23: wrote about social issues surrounding equality and freedom for all, within their community or internationally.

Winners

Age 6-11

	Prize	Title	Author (Age)/*Pseudonym*
1st	**£30**	**Freedom**	**Emma James** *1st Portchester Rainbows*
2nd	**£15**	**Two Girls**	**Eve Taylor-Reilly** *2nd Portchester Guides*
3rd	**£10**	**Freedom**	**Holly Ann Parks** *Silchester*

Age 12-15

	Prize	Title	Author (Age)/*Pseudonym*
1st	**£30**	**Freedom**	**Robert Black** *Signet-The Edge*
2nd	**£15**	**Freedom**	**Jamie Cowcher** *Woodside*
3rd	**£15**	**Freedom**	**C Harrington-Johnson** *1st Clanfield Guides*

Age 16-23

	Prize	Title	Author (Age)/*Pseudonym*
1st	**£30**	**Growing Upwards**	**Rose-Marie Roberts** *Warsash*
2nd	**£15**	**Freedom**	**Emma Macenri** *5th Porchester Guides*

The winning poems were read by the above named poets and the prizes were awarded at The Guildhall, Winchester by Mrs Mary Fagan, Lord Lieutenant of Hampshire on Tuesday, 2 October, 2004.

FREEDOM

EMMA JONES ~ AGE 6

I have been locked
in a cage
for quite a while.
It is better
than being eaten
by a crocodile.

Please can you
please can you
help me get
free
so that I can
fly up into
that tree.

ADJUDICATION

It seems to me that this competition proves the old adage that the greatest things come in the smallest packages. This poem has been constructed out of 13 lines and most of the lines have three words on them, one has four words and another has one word. The one word is 'free'. In the simplest of languages, the poem addresses the complex idea of freedom and what it might mean by seeing the positive side of being locked away, that at least you would not be eaten by a crocodile. The helplessness of captivity is emphasised in the pleas for release, two lines repeating the phrase 'Please can you/please can you/help me get/free./'

Keith Bennett

FREEDOM

Robert Black ~ Age 13

F is for freedom that everyone should get,

R is for reaching a target freedom set.

E is for everything that is free,

E is for everybody that wants it to be.

D is for decisions we all have to make

O is for options we all have to take,

M is for my freedom that I won't put at stake

Adjudication

This acrostic is an example of controlled writing. The poem uses rhyme and rhythm within the form to great effect. Every word is justified in its position in the line and every line could stand on its own, yet each works toward the whole subject of the poem.

The use of rhyming couplets, backed up with the three line end rhymes are evidence that thought has been used extensively in the development of the poem.

The final line, with its uncompromising stance, supports the strength of the whole poem. This is a first class piece of writing that is worthy of the first prize in the 12-15 age group.

Keith Bennett

GROWING UPWARDS

Rose-Marie Roberts ~ Age 17

The end of an era,
These twelve years are up,
The best years of my life, they said,
They were right, of course.
Millions of memories,
Parties, private jokes, first dates,
Outings, no need to control myself!
But Yay! Freedom at last!

Now I cry inwardly to myself,
Why did it all have to go so fast?
Faced with responsibilities, deadlines, decisions
If this is what they call freedom,
I don't want it,
I don't want to grow up.

ADJUDICATION

Peter Pan did not write this poem but he might've done. This is a wonderfully wry look at leaving school, that all children look forward to and the closing lines sum up the feelings succinctly.

The poem makes good use of cliché, opening with 'The end of an era' and following up two lines later with 'The best years of my life.' These work because the subject of the poem is well known, the discovery that those school days were more enjoyable than the grown-up world of work.

Finally the poem works because it does not lecture or moralize beyond the known clichés. It is a bald statement of fact and one with which many will identify. I liked this poem very much and I make it the winner of the 15-23 age group.

Keith Bennett

LifeWriting Competition

Sponsor:

The Joyce Morris Literacy Foundation &
The Queen's English Society

Adjudicators: Dr Joyce M Morris & Dr Bernard Lamb

WINNERS & HIGHLY COMMENDED

Competitors were invited to send the first page of writing and an outline of a biographical account. The style of writing was an important consideration in the awarding of the prizes.

Winners

	Prize	Title	Author (Age) / *Pseudonym*
1st	**£150**	**A Remarkable Woman: the Life of Dorothée Pullinger Lady Engineer**	**Mary Smith** *Helen Dunlop*
2nd	**£100**	**A Flight of Fancy**	**Carol Waterkeyn** *Caroline Wren*
3rd	**£50**	**To My Queen and Two Bits**	**Caroline Wigley** *Meriel F*

Highly Commended

Title	Author	Pseudonym
A Yorkshire Farm Labourer	**Marion Jordan**	*Tongue-Tied*
The Remarkable Dr Settler	**Garth Freeman**	*Brian Hicks*
You And Me	**Cariad**	*Gaynor Cohen*

THE LIFE OF DOROTHÉE PULLINGER

MARY SMITH

Three year old Dorothée and her mother clambered out of the trailer attached to the back of the motor tricycle. Aurelie smothered a sigh.

She had not realised how hilly parts of her native French countryside were. She smiled encouragingly at her daughter,

'Come on, ma petite this one is no bigger than the last,' she said.

Dorothée look mutinous. 'Oh come,' her father called, 'I bet you could reach the top of this hill almost as fast as I can.' Always eager to please her adored father the child smiled, tugging at her mother's hand even while she recognised the impossibility of the challenge. Thomas Pullinger shrugged apologetically at this wife as he restarted the motor tricycle. 'Not far, now,' he called as he chugged off in a cloud of dust. On the steepest of hills the tricycle struggled with the weight of its passengers. Thomas would wait for them at the top of the hill, where they would take their places in the trailer to resume the last part of their 500 kilometre journey from Lyon to Paris.

'When I grow up,' Dorothée said confidently, I'm going to be an engineer and help Papa make motor tricycles.' Her mother smiled at the idea. 'Tell me about his famous journey to Paris,' her daughter requested.

Panting slightly, Aurelie began the story her daughter had heard a thousand times. 'It was two years ago, in 1895,' she began, 'your father went to Germany to buy a motor cycle. He rode it all the way back from Munich to Paris. It was the very first motorcycle in France and thousands of people lined the streets of the city cheering and waving at your father and his wonderful machine. It was in all of the newspapers.

'Perhaps' mused her daughter, 'I shall even make motor cars.'

Against all odds and arguments from her father, Dorothée Pullinger achieved her ambition to become an engineer and by the 1920s she was indeed making motorcars.

Synopsis

The first section of the biography describes Dorothée Pullinger's early life in France, where she was born in 1894. As a young man, her father's first business venture, making and repairing bicycles, failed and he went to France with £5 in his pocket. His next venture in metal filament electric lamps also failed. By then he had married Aurelie and Dorothée was the first of 11 children. Throughout her life she worshipped her father.

He bought the first motorcycle to France, riding it from Munich to Paris and was subsequently invited to join a Lyon firm, where he built a car for the Sultan of Turkey. In 1900 he was awarded a gold medal for his design for an internal combustion engine at the Paris International Exhibition.

Dorothée was eight years old when the family (by then four younger brothers and sisters - the other six yet to come) moved to England. Dorothée, not knowing a word of English, was sent to Loughborough School for Girls.

Dorothée retained her ambition to become an engineer, something her father, who believed a girl's place was in the home, strongly opposed. For some years she remained at home until she finally persuaded her father to allow her into the drawing office of the new Arrol-Johnson factory in Dumfries, coming top in the exams she took along with the 'other boys.' During the war years Dorothée worked at Vickers in Barrow-in-Furness, supervising a 7,000 strong female workforce, who could build anything from a bicycle to a battleship. By the time she returned to Scotland after the war, Dorothée's father had become a staunch advocate for the 'fairer sex' becoming engineers. Dorothée was sent to manage a second Arrol-Johnson factory that, staffed mainly by women (tennis courts on the roof, piano and books in the staff room) was manufacturing cars. She also took part in field trials and motor racing and became a member of the Board of Directors.

In the mid-1920s Dorothée made a major career change. Accused by a journalist at the Motor Show of 'doing a man out of a job' she invested her savings in a laundry in Croydon since washing was women's work. By this time she had married. Her husband worked as a purser with the P & O line and the couple were apart for much of their early married life, during which time she built up an extremely successful business. During WWII she was invited, the only woman along with thirteen men, on the Government's Industrial Panel, advising on problems created by women war workers. A problem Dorothée insisted was because men 'were afraid of women workers'. When Dorothée decided to sell her business and retire to Guernsey, she promptly set about establishing a new, equally successful laundry business.

This biography does not only chronicle the extraordinary achievements of Dorothée, but it also provides an insight into the tensions between motherhood and her professional role. Dorothée was full of contradictions. She had a career at a time when women were expected to stay at home yet blamed rising divorce rates on there being 'no real homes any more'. She sent her own children away to boarding school, even leaving her son alone with the nuns during summer holidays when his school closed. The children also stayed with their grandparents for extended periods.

She could be penny-pinching to an extreme, especially in business yet loved buying luxuries and expensive clothes. Domestic staff did not stay and she was aware that much of the fault lay within herself, but she could not solve the problem. She was snobbish about connections, loved socialising, had a strong faith in both herself and God, all of which made Dorothée a remarkable woman whose story deserves to be told.

Adjudication

This should make an interesting book about a pioneering lady engineer. She comes over as a determined, successful but flawed character. The specimen page is fine but there are some errors in the synopsis, including a missed capital letter, some missing punctuation and an incomplete sentence. The adjudicators placed it second and third but finally agreed on it as the winner. Well done.

Dr Bernard Lamb

GENERAL RULES FOR SUBMITTING ENTRIES TO ALL OF THE COMPETITIONS AT EACH ANNUAL WRITERS' CONFERENCE

The General Competition Rules applies to all competitions. Specific competitions may have additional rules.

The short lists for all the competitions are posted at 1300 on Saturday at the conference. All the writing competition prizes are awarded and the adjudications announced at the Writers' Awards Reception at 1800 that evening.

1. The closing date for all competitions is the first Friday in June, except for *First Three Chapters of a Novel*, which is the last Friday in May.

2. The competition entry fee is £7 per entry for all categories for those attending the conference or entering the *Reaching Out* and / or *Childhood Between and During the Wars* Competitions. The competition fee is £9 per entry for those not attending the conference.

3. All entries must be written in English, original and unpublished work and must not have won an award in any previous competition.

4. Each entrant must provide **one new pseudonym** to identify all entries to all competitions. The pseudonym must not contain any part of the author's name.

5. Entries must be typed double-spaced, with the writer's pseudonym on the bottom right hand corner of every page. Author's names must be omitted from the manuscript.

6. Entrants are allowed to submit up to five entries for each competition unless otherwise stated.

7. The competition entry forms may be photocopied.

8. Copyright remains with the author.
9. Conference speakers are not allowed to enter the competitions.
10. A large stamped-addressed envelope must be provided for each competition entered (not one envelope for all entries) if competitors wish to have their entries returned. Adjudications will be attached to each submission. Pseudonyms must be marked on the bottom left-hand side of each reply envelope.
11. No responsibility will be taken by the Conference Director or University College Winchester for entries mislaid; competitors are advised to retain copies.
12. The decisions of the adjudicators are final and the adjudicators reserve the right to withhold awards if no entry reaches an appropriate standard.
13. First place winning entries for each competition will be published in the annual anthology. The winners are asked to send their *unaltered* manuscript in electronic format within 10 days following the conference. The editor reserves the right to correct manuscripts in accordance with the quality standard of *The Best of* series.

ADVICE ON ENTERING THE COMPETITIONS

To enhance your chances of winning when you prepare your entries for the competitions attached to the Annual Writers' Conference, it is suggested that you:

- Do read and comply with the terms of the competitions. Observe word counts, numbers of pages and the rules of presentation.
- Do proofread your manuscript for correct grammar and punctuation and spell check your manuscript on your computer. You may benefit from sharing your manuscript with others in your writing class or circle to ensure that your work is technically correct.

- Do read the entries of other competition winners and the adjudicators' notes. Many new ideas and learning points can be gained by studying their style, register, language, theme, point of view, characterization, plotting, setting and foreshadowing techniques and by observing the balance of dialogue and narrative. Use these observations as a benchmark for your own competitive writing.
- Do assess the cover, spine, design, typeface, ink and paper and size of book, if you are entering the Slim Volume, Limited Edition Competition.

The 25th Annual Writers' Conference Bookfair and Weeklong Workshops

24 June to 1 July, 2005
University College Winchester

The general rules for submitting entries are printed on the preceding pages, except for the following:

- The closing date for all competitions will be Friday, 3 June, 2005, except for the *First Three Chapters of the Novel*, Friday, 27 May, 2005.
- The competition entry fee will be £7 per entry for all categories for those attending the conference or entering the *Reaching Out Competition* and *Childhood Between and During the Wars*. The competition fee will be £9 per entry for those not attending the conference.

For details of the 25th Annual Writers' Competitions or Conference, Bookfair and Weeklong Workshops, please contact Mrs Barbara Large whose contact details are shown at the front of this edition.

From
Little Acorns
Mighty Writers Grow